Mental illness and mental handicap are **not** the same although they are ⟨grouped⟩ together under one heading.

Everybody experiences some sort of illness in their lives; you become il⟨l⟩ ⟨ ... ⟩ of some kind or through natural restorative processes.

Handicap is brain damage. A person is either born with a mental handic⟨ap⟩ ⟨or by⟩ physical illness, usually early in life. Someone who is mentally handicap⟨ped⟩ ⟨can develop to⟩ the limits of the handicap, depending how severe it is, but they can never get better.

This book is about MENTAL ILLNESS

SAME THING DAY AFTER DAY—⟨TU⟩BE—WORK—

DINNER—WORK—TUBE—ARMCHAIR—T.V.—SLEEP

TUBE—WORK—HOW MUCH MORE CAN

⟨Y⟩OU TAKE ONE IN TEN GO MAD—ONE IN FIVE CRACKS UP

MENTAL!

There's a label for you—as soon as the word appears in print everyone has some reaction to it. The reaction might be fear, it might be a strange fascination, it might be mirth, but, for all of us, it conjures up some images fixed in our minds by folklore or experience —how close the experience is will govern how accurate the images are.

The traditional images are the gaunt hospital on the hill outside the town, padded cells, sinister uncontrolled laughter, incoherent ravings, the man with his hat turned sideways and his hand stuffed inside his jacket who thinks he is Napoleon, jangling keys, being 'certified', electric shock treatment, whispering neighbours, a life sentence in the asylum.

If your experience—personal, within the family or because of the mental illness of a friend —has been different, then these hackneyed images may be distressing. They are not meant to be hurtful, but it is just as well to face the fact that they are still all too common and need breaking down and disproving.

We are all fascinated by our own minds and, even if we are not actively aware of it, we are all concerned with preserving our sanity in a 'mad' world. But there is no 'them and us', no mental apartheid. 'Them and us' are all of US.

It might be comforting to think, 'Everyone's daft except thee and me—and even thee's a bit queer' but we cannot draw a line and say, 'They are abnormal, we are normal', because:

Who's to say what is normal?

We have all been the central character in the little drama acted out at a bedside when the doctor takes a thermometer from our mouth, looks at it, and says to an anxious Mum, 'Good—back to normal'. But what does that mean?

It means that a column of mercury has climbed up a glass tube and registered 37° Centigrade, or something near it (98·4° on the Farenheit scale), a body

---

Does the dictionary definition help?

The Concise Oxford Dictionary gives us this:

Mental, a. & n. Of the mind; done by the mind as ~ arithmetic (performed without the use of written figures); (Colloq.) affected with ~ disorder; ~ patient (under care for disordered mind); ~ RESERVATION; ~ home, hospital, ASYLUM; (n. coloq.) ~ case or patient. Hence ~ LY adv. [ME, f.OF or LL mentalis (mens -ntis mind)]

So it is only colloquially that 'mental' has come to be synonymous with mad—'He's a mental case'. The basic definition is simply 'of the mind'. The reference to mental arithmetic is interesting,

and puts the word into proportion as just something going on within the mind. Think about this for a moment, do a bit of mental arithmetic, (say 27 + 14). It probably took you a fraction of a second but can you define what you did to reach an answer of 41? There was some element of memory, some of association, some of calculation but arriving at the answer was essentially a mysterious and little understood process within your brain —a process you can't identify, something complex taking place within your mind. It was a *mental* process.

temperature that medical science has defined as showing that you are reasonably healthy. This temperature is considered 'normal'. A lot of things can still be wrong with you even if you are 'normal' in this sense: a broken leg, a pulled muscle, a headache.

But 37° Centigrade is a useful base line, a point from which to start making judgements about our state of physical health. What about the state of our *mental* health? There is no neat base line for this. Everybody has his or her own characteristics so what is mentally 'normal'?

We are often quick to weigh up other people's behaviour and define it as mad or crazy or freaky or weird, but what do we mean? Do we mean any more 'unusual'? Do we mean that their behaviour embarrasses us? Do we just mean we don't understand it and so have to explain something outside our own experience as strange, threatening, 'abnormal'?

A latter-day Druid—at Tower Hill, London.

> 'Enter Tilburina stark mad in white satin and her confidante stark mad in white linen'
> Stage direction from the play *The Critic* by R. B. Sheridan (1751–1816)
>
> What do we, the audience, expect to see in the behaviour of Tilburina and her confidante? How do they demonstrate that they are 'stark mad'?

'PARROT SHOOT' AT A PARTY

GUESTS at a "very wild party" in a Scottish mansion fired shots at a pet parrot, a court heard yesterday.

Frog eater jumps clear

SELF - CONFESSED professional poacher Derek Podmore flapped into court yesterday in a frogman's suit with flippers, and with pheasant feathers behind his ears.

He pleaded not guilty to a charge under the Cruelty to Animals Act, 1911—to wit, swallowing a live frog in the lounge of the Railway Hotel, at Market Drayton, Shropshire.

Bristow: Frank Dickens

NANNIE— DID YOU HEAR THAT FUNNY MAN? HE WAS TALKING TO HIMSELF.....

FIRST SIGN OF MADNESS, TALKING TO YOURSELF....

Natural, but is it normal?

If we do judge that someone's behaviour is *ab*normal what do we mean? Is it just that we personally disagree with the way this person is behaving? Or perhaps it is that certain behaviour frightens us, and when we classify it as 'abnormal' we gain comfort by putting it into a category.

'Normal' is pretty dull really —it is unexceptional, a state without any highs or lows. 'How are things?' we say to a friend, 'Oh—going along normally', he or she says when there is nothing out of the ordinary to tell you.

The paradox of what we think of as normality is that it is dull and run-of-the-mill, yet something to be preserved. Do *you* like to be thought of as 'normal'? Does it have the same ring as 'ordinary' or 'boring'? Would you like people to think of you as 'abnormal'? Would it mean that you are more or less unusual, exciting, mysterious,—romantic even?

We each have different ideas on what is normal behaviour, so who is it makes the rules we abide by, however loosely? If normal equals acceptable, acceptable to whom?

There are state laws to deal with extremes of behaviour: drunk and disorderly, indecent exposure, assault. But most of the rules are unwritten, they have developed as society has evolved, become organized, become more stable, whatever that means. 'Normal' has come to mean 'that which does not offend against the norm in terms of behaviour', which is a definition that dodges the issue.

A lot of people would agree that society as a whole is too easily offended in this sense. Some people would say that the emphasis is on the quiet life: nothing intruding or annoying, keeping one's self to oneself, not being a nuisance to others. It's a pretty bleak formula for normality. Is this really the prevailing attitude? And is it so unreasonable?

An organized society has to have rules, both written and unwritten. Traditionally, rule-breakers were cast out of primitive societies because they threatened the stability (often a very fragile stability) of the rest of the group. Now we seek to 'correct' the rule-breakers although there is still a strong element of casting out in our attitude towards them.

Preservation of what has been built up or fought for *is* important, a thread of continuity is important to both an individual and to society as a whole to ensure consolidation and moving on to the next step. But barriers of acceptability or of permissiveness are not static; they keep being broken down and rebuilt in a different place almost from generation to generation. Acceptability moves in cycles; at the moment we are said to be moving out of an era of permissiveness back into a puritan revival. But, however we describe it we won't really be setting the clock back, simply going through another change.

So when talking about what is 'normal' we are in the world of value judgements, often a narrowly confined world. If someone's behaviour or life-style is unacceptable to society and to society's authorities is he necessarily abnormal? Is he 'a suitable case for treatment'? Morgan, in the film *Morgan–a Suitable Case for Treatment*, was desperately in love, immature, extravagant, inventive, persistent, impossible for his wife to live with, and a nuisance. He was not what you would call 'normal'. But would you call him 'abnormal', suffering from some form of mental disorder, and therefore not to be tolerated, and to be in need of control?

Morgan in a gorilla suit– 'a suitable case for treatment'?

Standards, conformity and eccentrics

Once standards are set, you treat them as things not only to aspire to, but also *to go beyond*, to be broken. That is as true for behaviour as it is for athletics or swimming. Conformity is something to kick against, to question, not to be accepted for its own sake. There is nothing intrinsically valuable about conformity. Standards and concepts of conformity are ill-defined boundaries, there to be tested out and prodded.

The most obvious group of rebels are the young, but their need to test and prod is somehow within the bounds of conformity. It is benevolently accepted as a necessary part of 'growing up'. However, this acceptance is being severely stretched, as the kicking against conformity becomes more profound, more contemptuous and destructive. Dropping out, communal living, soft drugs, hard drugs, anti-materialism, political militancy: all these to some degree symbolize rejection of accepted social values.

Apart from the young, not many people knowingly step over the boundaries of conformity. Eccentrics do, and we have a sneaking admiration of them for it. Eccentrics lack the inhibitions which hold most people back. They don't give a damn, they do what they want to do, they flaunt convention, they bring flamboyance and colour into an often drab world. They dare to act out their fantasies, and they force us to question our

standards of behaviour and our sense of values. Was Morgan a 'suitable case for treatment', or was he an eccentric? Was it simply his eccentricity that earned him the epithet, 'a suitable case'?

The 19th century was the great age of British eccentrics, many of them with great achievements in invention and exploration to their credit because they were so fiercely non-conformist. Lord Avon's father enjoyed —and that is the right word —a reputation as an eccentric. One story told of him is that one day, when it was pouring with rain, he went to look at the barometer hanging in his study. Its pointer was firmly fixed on 'Set Fair' so he took it off the wall and flung it through a closed window into the rain shouting, 'There you damned fool—see for yourself!'

It's an odd story. It also makes a couple of interesting assumptions about eccentrics. One: that he was sufficiently rich not to think twice about smashing both a window and a barometer, and two: that people would accept the action as that of an acknowledged eccentric whose position in society was assured.

There is a man who patrols Oxford Street on most fine days carrying above his head a placard saying that 'Protein and Passion are to blame for the ills of the world'. There is no doubt that he believes he has an important message for us all, which we are ignoring at our peril. What he says is scientifically without foundation, as far as we know, but stranger discoveries have been made in the course of medical history. For centuries anyone who maintained that blood circulated around the body pumped by the heart would have been thought eccentric.

Our attitude towards eccentrics varies enormously depending upon their behaviour, who they are, and what they are proclaiming. We may ridicule but we are usually tolerant. You may twist a finger against your temple to signify 'screwy' but you probably smile too, glad of the diversion, glad to have seen something out of the ordinary to throw into conversation with your friends.

But we would be uneasy if a placard carrier started to take any direct action, clutching our arm and trying to convince us of his message by talking directly to us. This kind of eccentricity is only acceptable at long range; when it gets to close quarters it becomes threatening, embarrassing, even frightening, and something to be shunned.

In Britain we live in a tolerant society by any standards (standards again), but how close are eccentrics to being 'mentally ill'? Their behaviour is often no more strange than that of people whom we feel obliged to classify as ill and try to treat.

Most famous eccentrics are or were rich—what happens to the ones who aren't rich? What happened to all the poor 19th century eccentrics? Were they put into mental hospitals 'for their own good'? Today it is the rich and famous who have almost fashionable 'nervous breakdowns', the rest of us have mental illnesses and are treated under the National Health Service. 'Nervous breakdown' is just a refined euphemism for mental illness which, somehow, has a sort of status and a faintly exclusive feeling about it. Most people avoid the actual words 'mental illness' when talking about it. Think how many such euphemisms you have encountered.

The 'Noah' of Washington Mud Flats calculated that the second flood would come in 1947 and built an ark large enough to contain everything he considered worth saving —including a full orchestra.

'Camberley Kate' exercising her stray dogs.

7

Acts of madness

How often have you heard the expression, 'That was a mad thing to do!' It usually means that someone who hasn't got a reputation for strange behaviour, someone 'normal' in fact, has done something unexpected, quite out of character.

It also means 'mad' in the colloquial sense: zany, inexplicable. It may be said with a tinge of delight or amusement about: jumping into a fountain on a winter's night, picking dahlias from the corporation's floral clock and presenting them to your girl friend, or shouting 'Come home Daddy, all is forgiven' to the policeman on the corner.

An act of madness in a suburban street in Oxford. After ringing the police several times, Eric Malloy, a demolition expert, finally blew himself and his whole house up.

If someone 'acts mad' once or twice it is just an endearing extension of his or her personality. If it becomes a regular part of their behaviour they may come to be regarded as eccentric. If they do so virtually all the time, calling them 'mad' can stop being colloquial and affectionate and start to become a real value judgement, a classification,—a condemnation.

Before Flower Power and the Beautiful People in the late 1960s, habitually walking barefoot along city streets was sufficient reason for being called 'mad'— now it hardly warrants a second glance.

In Korea in 1952, Sgt. William Roberts' platoon was pinned down by a North Korean machine-gun nest. They had been under heavy fire for two hours when suddenly the Sergeant scrambled out of the ditch, ran and rolled 50 yards through a hail of gun fire, before lobbing a hand grenade into the nest killing the enemy gun crew. He got a medal. He was not an exceptional man, just a good professional soldier. Was this an act of madness?

John Dryden, the 17th century poet, coined the expression 'heroically mad' and the history of warfare and catastrophe is full of people who, for a few moments, become heroically mad. Anger and frustration must contribute to moments like this when the reflex of self-preservation is short-circuited.

So we all have the potential within us to perform an 'act of madness', just as we all carry about with us the raw material for mental illness in our everyday moods and emotions.

'One mad action is not enough to prove a man mad.' English proverb from a collection made in 1732

We are all emotional

Emotions, feelings and sensitivity are 'normal'; we all have them and we all need them to cope with the world around us day by day. They are common to every one of us, although some people seem to have less than others or, at least, *show* them less than others.

Everybody has fluctuating moods and feelings, reacting with innumerable variations to events and situations from day to day. We are all familiar with our moods being shaped by external and internal factors: 'Monday morning blues', that 'Friday afternoon feeling' of laziness looking forward to the weekend, the anxiety felt before a new date or an exam, the depression of January with Christmas over.

Our mental resources are constantly interacting with our physical resources and the influence of outside events and situations to maintain a balance called health or stability or normality. We all show and experience a great range of behaviour, sometimes depression is dominant for a while, sometimes elation or expectation, sometimes anxiety, sometimes calm. Any one of these feelings can last for days, depending upon degrees of stress or relaxation but, all the time, other feelings of relief, of happiness, of doubt, will be intervening every now and then to maintain a balance, to keep a perspective.

So our mental health, staying sane if you like, depends upon a constant balancing act of checks, counter-checks and responses. Mental ill health begins when there is an imbalance, when emotions, feelings and sensitivity run unchecked and one becomes dominant to the exclusion of others. As long as the balance is maintained by a wide variety of moods and feelings we are all right, when just one or two take over we are in trouble. Hence the apparently paradoxical logic behind the English proverb from a collection made in 1670 'You will never be mad, you are of so many minds'.

The best illustration of a dominant emotion affecting judgement and destroying balance —used since time immemorial in drama, poetry, prose and now pop music —is love. People have been falling 'madly in love' for centuries: totally absorbed in each other, oblivious of their surroundings, constantly elated, not eating or sleeping. Literature is also full of pathetic, distracted figures driven mad with love, unrequited, forbidden, illicit love. It is a very powerful emotion which can bring with it strong feelings of jealousy and hate.

Shakespeare has Puck in *A Midsummer Night's Dream* telling us

'Cupid is a knavish lad
Thus to make poor females mad.'

which is a light-hearted and romantic reference to love. But he also has Ophelia driven mad by Hamlet's rejection of her love, and the death of her father. In an age when insanity was poorly understood Shakespeare describes Ophelia's madness with almost clinical accuracy

Pop music perpetuates the idea of people driven to extreme by love with titles like 'I think I'm going out of my mind over you'. So the idea of emotional imbalance leading to disorders of the mind is firmly fixed both in our historical and contemporary culture, although whether we take it seriously, and actually think about it in these terms is dubious.

Just as we all rely on our emotions and feelings to pilot us through life, we all carry the ingredients (those same emotions and feelings) for mental illness around with us. We are all vulnerable to some extent although it is important to make it clear here and now, that mental illnesses are NOT contagious or infectious. It also has to be said that, more often than not, more than one factor is involved in the origins of a neurotic mental illness.

Mary is twenty-four, neat, small, brown-haired, pretty and rather shy. She has been married for two years to Frank, who is two years older than her. He is a sales representative whose work takes him away from home overnight about once a week. They moved into their first house six months ago, a new three-bedroomed 'semi' on a new estate on the outskirts of Bristol. Getting the deposit together was quite a struggle and Mary went on working as a clerk in an Insurance Office to help. Now that the mortgage rate has increased they are financially stretched. Despite this Frank has insisted that Mary stops work now that they have a home of their own.

Mary is a bit of a worrier, her mother always told people she was 'highly strung', a very sensitive girl. The family was always very close but six months ago Mary's father was promoted to a job in Southampton, and the easy casual visits to see each other have come to an end.

Mary is house proud but the housework does not take long; there isn't much furniture and what there is has been mostly handed down from relatives. The other wives in the street either go out to work or are very preoccupied with small children and Mary feels a bit isolated during the day.

For about two months now she has been feeling strangely depressed, it's particularly bad on the nights when Frank is away. She doesn't eat very well—partly to save money and partly because she doesn't fancy food much. Despite her efforts to make the house as clean and nice as possible, dishes have begun to pile up in the sink. She watches television a lot during the day as well as at night. She's beginning to lose interest in her appearance and she's beginning to lose interest in sex, which makes Frank grumpy. This, in turn, makes her feel more depressed. Frank has also begun to criticize her cooking which is becoming more and more careless and uninteresting because she has no enthusiasm for it.

Frank is a bit bewildered about the change which is coming over Mary and is now urging her to go and see the doctor although she insists there is nothing wrong with her. Secretly she is worrying about how she feels and is trying to pluck up the courage to go to the doctor but she doesn't know what she would complain of once she did get to the surgery.

The beginnings of Mary's mental illness are an extension of normality, of the feeling of depression.

Death ended incurable sadness of Harlech heir

DOCTORS knew no cure for the sadness that haunted Julian Ormsby Gore, elegant young heir to the Harlech title and fortune.

Psychiatrists, electric shock treatment and psychotherapists all failed to lift the depression that dogged him for ten years. And a coroner today recorded that he took his own life as a result of his illness.

His suicide bid ruined a pilot's career

A DESPERATELY lonely salesman tried to kill himself in a head-on car crash, a court heard yesterday.

The death-wish driver survived and recovered.

But ironically his innocent victim's career as an RAF pilot was ended by injuries inflicted in the crash.

The salesman, 26 - year - old Peter Stankiewicz, had tried several times before to commit suicide.

Six-month rest for Parkinson

TV STAR Michael Parkinson is to take a complete break from work for six months because of exhaustion.

A business associate said last night: "Mike is near to a nervous breakdown. He has been overdoing work and he has already cancelled all his engagements for the next two weeks."

Parkinson, aged 39, who lives near Windsor, Berks, said he would not work until his next television series started.

He added : " But I'm no basket-weaving case."

He astonished viewers with a verbal attack on two journalists in his final TV chat show last Saturday.

Parkinson . . . overwork

The spectrum of mental illness

Health is not a firmly definable state. Probably no one is perfectly healthy both physically and mentally. There are ups and downs day by day. We can all put up with sore throats, stiff backs, skin rashes, feeling 'one degree under'; they may mar our work or our leisure but we don't take to our beds, we are not incapacitated by them.

It is the same with mental illness. Just as most mentally ill people have periods of stability and insight, 'normal' people have feelings of irrational anxiety and depression. What we call mental 'illness' is a point on a spectrum with, at one end, an ill-defined state of mental health ('normality'), and, at the other, severe mental ill health ('abnormality').

We all live our lives in states of mental health or ill health at various points along this spectrum. Some of us may always be firmly within the mentally healthy area. Some may move back and forth between mental illness and mental health, a few move into the area of mental illness, move about within it but never get back into a state of mental health. A small number move to the extremes of severe mental ill health and stay at that point for the rest of their lives.

'All the physicians and authors in the world could not give a clear account of his madness. He is mad in patches, full of lucid intervals.'
Said of Don Quixote by Miguel Cervantes 1547–1616

GOLDEN HOARD OF THE MAGPIE POSTMAN

POSTMAN John Gillam could outshine any magpie when it came to hoarding treasure.

Other people's treasure, that is.

For during his three years as a postie he helped himself to property worth a staggering £17,000.

In one year he was stealing postal packets at the rate of a hundred a week.

His golden hoard, which included jewellery, fancy goods and clothing, was found stacked in a cellar at his home.

It took three vans to cart the secret treasure trove away.

Yesterday, at Dudley Crown Court, Worcs, Gillam admitted four specimen charges of stealing postal packets.

He asked for another charge involving £17,000-worth of goods to be taken into account.

Gillam, 29, was said to have told police: "I don't know why I did it. It was just a habit."

His counsel, Mr. Martin Wilson, told the court: "He was behaving rather like a magpie.

"He was stealing bright shiny objects like jewellery and hoarding them obsessively without any gain for himself."

Teacher's death protest

A teacher went to pieces and died a nervous wreck when she believed that she had been put under observation by the Special Branch.

In five months, she lost six stone and finally her body was found in a pond on Clapham Common, South London, an inquest at Battersea was told yesterday.

Mrs Sheila Burns, aged 46, kept a diary in which she recorded the times she thought she was kept under observation. The first entry was made in July. It said: "Followed by SB?"

Tragedy of the Mum who tried too hard

PERFECT wife and mother Ann Wilson kept her home spotless and showered affection on her family.

But the strain of being a Super-mum became too much and she decided to kill herself and her three children.

She slashed her three-year-old daughter Gillian's wrists in the bathroom.

But the sight of the wound she had inflicted was enough to stop her harming her other daughter and son.

She called for help—and when it arrived she was cuddling Gillian, trying to stop the flow of blood.

Yesterday a court heard how such a wonderful wife could have even contemplated harming her family.

BREAKDOWN

ABOUT TWO YEARS AGO, in my mid-forties, I had a sudden and severe mental breakdown. There was nothing unusual about the breakdown nor about the events in my own life that led up to it. The only unusual feature of the case was that I am myself a psychologist and was able to view the events from both sides of the fence. Although one in six women and one in nine men spend some part of their lives as an in-patient in a psychiatric hospital, there is still a formidable degree of ignorance and prejudice surrounding mental illness and its treatment.

The immediate cause of my breakdown lay in an event of too personal a nature to enter into here. It seems in retrospect that, given my psychological make-up, it was tailor-made to cause me the maximum possible hurt. Within a period of twenty-four hours, my life disintegrated and I changed from being cheerful, outgoing and continually active into someone who was a prey to the most tortured thoughts and self-recriminations with neither interest in nor ability to cope with the outside world.

My thoughts were so obsessive that I lost all ability to concentrate. For five months I was virtually unable to read even the daily paper. I tried to force myself to study but the effort was hopeless and there was one book on psychology that I must have started several hundred times, but I never succeeded in getting past the first page and even that I was unable to understand. One of the consequences of being unable to read or to follow a film or play was the most extreme boredom. There was nothing to look forward to except fitful bouts of sleep and I lived in a hell of anxiety and boredom.

Types of mental illness

Mental illnesses do not classify into neat, water-tight compartments. What may begin as a minor phobia can develop into a severe depression. What may appear at first to be a bad schizophrenic disorder may subsequently become a much less serious state of anxiety.

For the purposes of simplification, mental illnesses can be broken into two groups: **neuroses** (minor but possibly lasting for a long time), and **psychoses** (major but possibly lasting only a short time). Whatever the classification, it is important always to remember that even in the depths of a mental illness there are still periods of normality and lucidity.

Neuroses

Neurotic depression and Anxiety states
an extension and dominance of the normal moods of depression and anxiety common to us all.

Phobias
anxiety state about something specific (birds, confined spaces, etc.), an irrational fear which the sufferer knows is illogical but cannot control.

Hysteria
periods of uncontrolled emotional outbursts (now widely doubted to be a type of mental illness at all).

Obsession
unreasonable preoccupation or repetition; for example a compulsion to wash and re-wash your hands, or return to the house to check and re-check that the gas is off.

Nervous breakdown
general euphemism usually for neurotic depression or depression and anxiety which often occur in the same illness in more or less equal parts. Often popularly linked to general and ill-defined 'stress'.

Psychoses

Endogenous depression
far more profound, totally incapacitating form of depression, feelings of 'worthlessness' and self-hatred, high risk of suicide.

Manic-depression
violent swings of mood between elation (optimisim, enormous self-confident exuberance) and depression with same characteristics as above. Often there is a clear cycle of mania-depression-mania, sometimes long periods of one or the other, frequent long periods of complete normality between 'bouts'.

Paranoia
irrational feelings of being persecuted, hunted, terrorized either by everyone and everything *or* by specific individuals or groups *or* by inanimate or alien forces (radio waves, the Martians, etc.). Delusions, voices.

The 'Schizophrenias'
little understood, profound mental disturbances, not acknowledged as an 'illness' by some doctors. NOT split personality but rather having a fantasy existence and a reality existence both of which are equally real, often accompanied by delusions, voices, sometimes hallucinations, bizarre imagery.

Senile dementia
vagueness and disorientation which comes with the acceleration of degenerative process in old age. Rate of degeneration varies enormously and senile dementia is *not* an inevitable part of ageing.

Another generalization in the interests of simplification is that for the **neurotic** disorders the character of reality remains the same while in the **psychotic** disorders the very nature of reality changes. But there will be flashes of normality throughout, and, in the case of the schizophrenias, reality and fantasy exist side by side and a person can be in either 'world' within the space of an hour.

Personality disorders

Not 'illnesses' at all in the accepted sense, personality disorders are more a case of poor social development and being unable to adapt to or coexist with the rest of society without constant conflict (these used to be called **psychopathic personalities**).

Personality disorders often result from isolation, parental neglect or general deprivation. Within this category are people 'condemned' as **inadequate personalities**. As a group they have an undeserved reputation for violence (psychopaths), which comes from the well-publicized minority who do commit offences. Also increasingly known as **sociopaths**.

Psychosomatic disorders

Not really 'mental' illness, rather a case of emotional changes causing body changes. For instance the anxiety of an exam candidate may lead to feelings of nausea, trembling, sweating, palpitations, or wanting to go to the lavatory.

Other illnesses in which the psychosomatic mechanism of the mind influencing the body is thought to play a part are : migraine, asthma, peptic ulcers, ulcerative colitis and some skin diseases. Treatment for these disorders is given by the relevant medical specialist in the physical illness, although this specialist may well call in a psychiatrist to advise on the mental aspects of the illness, or the patient may ask to see a psychiatrist as well.

Misconceptions

Madness at full moon.

Before reading any further, stop and build up in your mind's eye your own picture of a madman or someone who is mentally ill. (Are they separated in your imagination, anyway?) What comes to mind will depend on how distant or how close your own exposure to mental illness happens to be.

Now compare the picture you have built up with this classical evocation of madness, probably the most famous in all of Victorian literature, from *Jane Eyre:*

'He lifted the hangings from the wall, uncovering the second door : this, too, he opened. In a room without a window, there burnt a fire, guarded by a high and strong fender, and a lamp suspended from the ceiling by a chain. Grace Poole bent over the fire, apparently cooking something in a saucepan. In the shade, at the further end of the room, a figure ran backwards and forwards. What it was, whether beast or human being, one could not, at first sight, tell; it grovelled, seemingly on all fours; it snatched and growled like some strange wild animal: but it was covered with clothing; and a quantity of dark, grizzled hair, wild as a mane, hid its head and face.

"Good-morrow, Mrs. Poole!" said Mr. Rochester. "How are you? and how is your charge today?"

"We're tolerable, Sir, I thank you," replied Grace, lifting the boiling mess carefully on to the hob: "rather snappish, but not 'rageous'."

A fierce cry seemed to give the lie to her favourable report: the clothed hyena rose up, and stood tall on its hind feet.

"Ah sir, she sees you!" exclaimed Grace : "You'd better not stay."

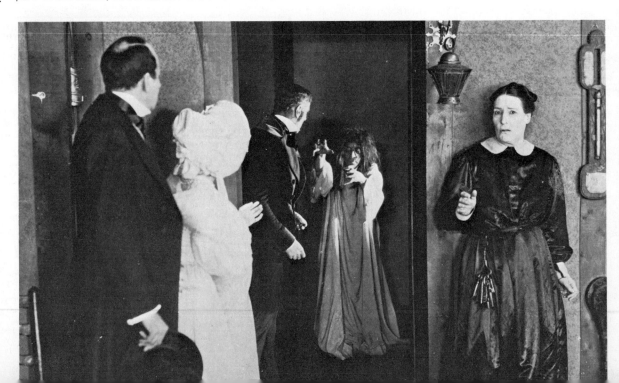

An early film interpretation of the confrontation with Mrs Rochester in Jane Eyre.

"Only a few moments, Grace : you must allow me a few moments."

"Take care then, sir!—for God's sake, take care!" The maniac bellowed: she parted her shaggy locks from her visage, and gazed wildly at her visitors. I recognized well that purple face,—those bloated features. Mrs. Poole advanced.

"Keep out of the way", said Mr. Rochester, thrusting her aside : "she has no knife now, I suppose? and I'm on my guard."

"One never knows what she has, sir: she is so cunning it is not in mortal discretion to fathom her craft."

"We had better leave her," whispered Mason.

"Go to the devil!" was his brother-in-law's recommendation.

"Ware!" cried Grace. The three gentlemen retreated simultaneously. Mr. Rochester flung me behind him: the lunatic sprang and grappled his throat viciously, and laid her teeth to his cheek: they struggled. She was a big woman, in stature almost equalling her husband, and corpulent besides: she showed virile force in the contest—more than once she almost throttled him, athletic as he was. He could have settled her with a well-planted blow; but he would not strike: he would only wrestle. At last he mastered her arms; Grace Poole gave him a cord, and he pinioned them behind her: with more rope, which was at hand, he bound her to a chair. The operation was performed amidst the fiercest yells, and the most convulsive plunges. Mr. Rochester turned to the spectators: he looked at them with a smile both acrid and desolate.

"That is *my wife*" he said. "Such is the sole conjugal embrace I am ever to know—such are the endearments which are to solace my leisure hours!"

Charlotte Bronte *Jane Eyre*

The impression in your own mind *should* be very different from this terrifying encounter with the mad Mrs Rochester in the attic of Thornfield Hall but

there may be persistent linking threads with this archetypal picture of madness:

- **appearance**: the clothing, the wild mane of hair, the wild gaze, the 'bloated' features
- **movement** : grovelling, springing forward, convulsive plunges
- **sound** : growling, crying, bellowing, fierce yelling
- **violence** : grappling, laying 'her teeth to his cheek', struggling
- **other traits**: incredible cunning

All these features are extreme in the case of Mrs Rochester but they are elements we have almost come to expect from madness or mental illness because of impressions gained from literature, from film and TV.

One man, two personalities; the gentle Dr Jekyll and the ferocious Mr Hyde. This film can be held largely responsible for establishing in the public mind the erroneous idea that schizophrenia is simply split personality.

This brilliant evocation of madness, together with other portrayals in fiction, has done a long-term disservice to our present-day image of mental illness. We still suffer from a 'hang-over' of the expectations of previous generations—predominantly the Victorians since they built most of the existing hospitals and set the pattern of treatment and social attitudes towards the mentally ill.

The fiction of today, and particularly film and TV output, often persists in presenting the traditional frightening, eerie portrayal of madness—something dramatic and extreme : the psychopath at large with an axe; the paranoiac determined to destroy his imagined persecutors before they get to him; the beautiful girl lost within her depression about to leap into the Thames. These types of madness all exist, but they are rare; they are well into the abnormal part of the spectrum of mental illness.

The vast majority of people who are mentally ill are not a danger to the public; they do not behave wildly in any way. Our impressions are often clouded by ignorance, fear, superstition and stigma.

Take James Wilkins. Twenty-one years old, in his final year at university. Intelligent but not brilliant, he has to work hard to keep up with his Modern Languages course. He is not bad looking, quiet, enjoys playing and watching football, and is also interested in politics and films. Three months before final exams, his girl-friend dropped him. His revision suffered immediately. A week later he heard that his father had to go into hospital for an exploratory operation to find out whether a tumour was cancerous or benign. His work stopped completely for a week, he went home but was urged by his parents to return to university and prepare for his finals. He tried, but was totally unable to concentrate. He got some pills from the university medical centre but by now, well into a state of anxiety and depression, he was beginning to contemplate suicide.

James was becoming mentally ill but was totally inconspicuous, a danger to no one but himself. But for a friend putting him in touch with the Nightline Service (a kind of university campus-based Samaritans), he might well have killed himself, and he would certainly have descended into a severe breakdown. As it is, he responded to out-patient psychiatric treatment and was allowed to defer his finals.

James' experience of mental illness was quiet, contained within him; there was no bizarre behaviour to bring it to the attention of others. It was almost unnoticeable but none the less potentially serious, and possibly fatal for him.

Enid Thompkins is middle-aged and lives in a luxury flat in a Sussex sea-side resort. Her husband is a senior company executive who has little time for her any more. He spends his spare time on the golf course and going to the theatre in London, an interest Enid doesn't share. They have one son, in the Merchant Navy, who is seldom home.

The luxury flat was bought by her husband as a kind of offering, in the knowledge that he devoted little time to his wife. Enid had time on her hands, and filled it by keeping the flat looking like something out of the Ideal Home Exhibition. A couple of years ago her menopause started and she began to become anxious and edgy. Keeping the flat spotless became an obsession, although she was unaware of it.

If her husband brings a guest to the flat, which he does rarely, or if Enid is visited by a friend she cannot relax. She plumps cushions, almost seeming to resent the dents put into them when the guest leans back in a chair; at the first trace of cigarette ash she whisks the ash tray away to wash it; a drink spilt on the carpet amounts to a major disaster.

The window cleaner is booked twice a week. Enid dusts and polishes the furniture at least twice a day. Carpets are professionally cleaned every three months.

The obsession about cleanliness makes living in the flat well-nigh unbearable for Enid's husband, and adds to his determination to spend as little time there as possible.

Enid has developed an obsessional neurosis but it goes unnoticed as such by her husband who puts it down to boredom and menopause. Enid's friends think of her as excessively house-proud, but not ill, and would not dream of recommending that she sees a doctor. Her life has become dominated by her obsession and is likely to stay that way.

Suicide and the peril of the young

SINCE 1963, the suicide statistics as a whole for Great Britain have dropped by about a third. In the 15-24 age group, however, they have remained more or less constant.

In 1972, 53 boys and 36 girls, aged between 15 and 19, and 169 boys and 63 girls, aged between 20 and 24, took their own lives, making suicide the second highest cause of death for youngsters in this age range.

The figures, though shocking, only represent the tip of the iceberg as a measure of adolescent despair.

It is estimated that for every achieved suicide, there are 99 failed attempts, plus, of course, the many thousands who—teetering on the brink of wanting-to-live, wanting-to-die — pick up the phone and dial the Samaritans or a university nightline.

Dr Richard Fox, consultant psychiatrist at Severalls Hospital in Colchester, who has made a special study of suicide and the young, found that relationship difficulties with parents plus loneliness are paramount causes of depression.

However, worries about homosexuality are an increasing trend and death of a parent—particularly the father — is an established correlate of suicidal tendencies.

Exam pressures and the failure to meet the expectations of parents inevitably emerge among the key tensions of student life.

In this case Enid's neurosis is typified by an exaggeration of normal behaviour but it will almost certainly go unrecognized and, although it fills her time, it fills it with something essentially inconsequential, and the quality of her life is impoverished by it.

Enid and James are typical—not Mrs Rochester. Most mental illness is typified by dullness, anxiety, despair, apathy, and by a general flattening out and damping down of behaviour patterns, rather than any heightening or exaggeration of behaviour. There is seldom any 'raving about' involved in being mentally ill.

'Madman'

From primitive times (and, it can be argued, right up to the present day) the madman has been a convenient scapegoat, somebody set apart and alienated from his social group by his behaviour. By virtue of already being *seen* to be set apart, it has always been conveniently simple to attach blame to the madman for a wide variety of ills within a society and drive him from that society. We still do this, we simply do it in a sophisticated and official manner which somehow makes it seem all right.

Hippocrates, the father of Greek medicine, insisted around 400 B.C. that all forms of insanity had natural causes. He gave clearly recognizable accounts of melancholia, mania, paranoias and hysteria.

The accidents with the cart and the young pigs drowning are typical of events blamed on witches in the 17th century. The witches are shown being punished by being 'floated' and ducked.

In the age of Alexandrian Greek medicine during the second century B.C., Asclepiades drew careful distinctions between the delirium of fever and the delusions of the insane. He despised the term 'insanity' as unscientific and held that mental illness was due to intolerable emotional disturbances. He and his pupil Themison had most advanced ideas about the care and treatment of patients. You would rather have been treated by them than by any psychiatrist for the next 1900 years.

The long dark ages of psychiatry were just around the corner. In medieval times, some kinder monks and nuns cared well for the mentally sick, but the official treatment was generally some form of exorcism. Madness was possession by demons, and the treatment was torment to make the fiends' temporary residence in man's body too uncomfortable for him.

The great epidemic of witch-hunting submerged medieval psychiatry and the 'Malleus Maleficarum' or Hammer of Witches, compiled in the 1470s became the psychiatric text book of the Inquisition for the next two centuries. A basic standpoint of this extraordinary work, in which insanity and religious heresy are so strangely fused, was that 'all witchcraft comes from carnal lust which in women is insatiable'.

Of course, there were notable exceptions to the European pattern of torture, exorcism, burning and scapegoating. Arab psychiatry during the European dark ages seems to have a much brighter record. In Cairo there was an asylum where 20 patients were looked after by 150 attendants. Amenities included music and dancing, concerts with clowns and tumblers, and delicious food. Recovered patients were given a bag of gold pieces to help them through the first economic stresses of the outside world. Yet in 1398, in London's recently founded Bedlam Asylum, the inventory of equipment for the few patients began '4 prs manacles, 11 chains of iron, 2 prs stocks'.

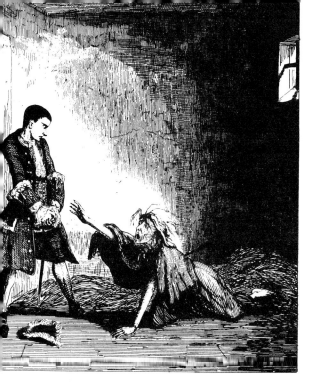

An 18th century depiction of madness: a young man visits his lunatic mother in an asylum.

A view of Bedlam by Hogarth.

In Britain no serious attempts to *treat* mental illness were made until the 18th century although there was a period in the 17th century when blood 'transfusions' for depression, and blood letting for mania were fashionable. In the 18th century, psychiatry was marked by some alarming shock treatments. In England Dr John Brown, and later in America, Dr Benjamin Rush, seem to have been sincere in their use of trap-doors which opened unexpectedly under patients' feet and dropped them into cold water! The twirling stool was also popular; a device in which the patient was revolved until half-dead from dizziness.

The 'non-injurious torture' devised by John Christian Reil involved not only duckings and the firing of small cannon to shock a patient back to his senses, but also having members of the hospital staff dressed up 'as judges, angels, the dead newly risen from their graves'.

In England public attitudes towards mental illness remained barbarous throughout the 18th century. A trip to Bedlam to watch the antics of the lunatics,

who were exhibited by their keepers, was a popular Sunday afternoon diversion well into the 19th century.

Dr Willis, who attended George III (originally diagnosed as manic-depressive but now thought to have suffered from a rare physical disorder), had no hesitation in knocking his royal patient down, wrapping him in a straitjacket and blistering him until he yelled. Yet Willis had a reputation for being progressive. Official reports of both York and Bedlam asylums around 1815 make shocking reading with accounts of patients chained up for years in cells on bedding of filthy straw saturated with urine and excrement.

The great day in the history of mental hospital reform had already dawned in France on 25th August, 1793, when the humane and enlightened Philippe Pinel, newly appointed Superintendent of the asylum at Bicetre, insisted on unchaining 53 patients and demonstrating that they were much better for it. In England the movement for proper treatment and the abolition of restraint got under way rather later.

A 'New Asylum for Idiots' opened in 1854 at Earlswood Common, Surrey.

The Victorian legacy

Large, austere mental hospitals—many still in use—were built by the Victorians to cope with the rising urban population. They were designed as places of custody, more for observing and controlling large numbers of patients, than for their comfort or care. The 'bear pit' system, under which chronic patients were turned out for an afternoon airing into a paddock surrounded by high fences, where they wandered about aimlessly, scratched in the soil with sticks or listlessly stood about, still existed in some backward, understaffed county mental hospitals in the 1920s. These are the hospitals recalled by our grandparents and talked of within families to this day, which goes a long way to explain the continued fear and stigma attached to 'the asylum on the hill'.

Progress in psychiatry between 400 B.C. and the second half of the 19th century was negligible. In comparative terms, the leap forward after 1850 was immense. There was a rash of new classifications of disorders although the late-Victorian medical theorists got bogged down with ideas like 'volitional insanity' and 'moral imbecility'. Dark words about mental illness as God's retribution for immorality were bandied about. These harsh and puritanical doctrines were absorbed into the folklore and leave us with a hang-over effect which still colours attitudes. Our tendency to condemn the mentally ill, 'It's her own fault' and 'It's only what he deserves', stems from this period of severity and often hypocritical, religious righteousness.

A system of classifying illness by symptoms, based on very close observation, was devised in 1894 by the

Admission of Patients.

Classes of Patients.

That the several persons to be admitted into this Asylum be divided into the following Classes:

CLASS 1.—Lunatics of a superior rank, who shall contribute to the general charges of care and maintenance according to their pecuniary abilities.

2.—Lunatics, not actually paupers, supported partly by their friends, and partly out of the Subscription Funds.

3.—Pauper Lunatics.

4.—Vagrant Lunatics. } Sent to the Asylum by the order of the Justices under the authority of the Act.

5.—Criminal Lunatics.

6.—Dangerous Idiots.

AS TO THE
ADMISSION OF LUNATICS.

I.—That previously to the admission of Lunatics of the first Class, the weekly sum to be paid for each be settled, and security given

Flowers and animals made conditions a bit more tolerable at Bedlam in 1860.

'Rules and Regulations for the Government of the General Lunatic Asylum of the County of Stafford' 1824. Treatment and comfort depended on the wealth of the patient.

great German clinical psychiatrist, Kraepelin. Freud's
interpretation of the role of the unconscious began to
provide a key to the understanding of symptoms which
had seemed meaningless, and this interpretative
approach was carried out by Professor Eugen Bleuler
in Zurich as a basis for treatment of neuroses. Management of mental hospitals remained largely custodial,
with locked wards for chronic and disturbed patients,
until the 1940s. The modern 'open-door' movement,
which started at Warlingham Park, Surrey, in 1942,
grew rapidly in prestige and influence.

Another aspect of the revolution in psychiatry came
with the development of intensive physical treatments
in the 1930s, first with insulin treatment for 'the
schizophrenias', and then the use of ECT (electro-
convulsive therapy). This reduced the time spent in
hospital by patients suffering from schizophrenia and
other predominantly depressive illnesses by 70%,
although its suitability for many cases remains highly
controversial to this day.

The final aspect of the 'treatment revolution' dates
from the mid-1950s with the introduction of new
tranquillizing drugs. Their effect of calming without
stupifying, excitable patients, and bringing chronic
patients back within reach of contact, and into the
recoverable category has gone a long way towards
transforming the modern mental hospital. Even so,
these comparatively new treatments have brought
with them a whole new set of medical and ethical
problems (considered later in this book).

Mad-men in history

Ludwig

Ludwig II was known as the 'mad' king of Bavaria. A sensitive child, he suffered a harsh upbringing and came to the throne at the age of eighteen. He was passionately devoted to music, architecture and other visual arts. He encouraged and patronized Wagner whom he idolized. He built the most beautiful dream-like castles, but he emptied the governmental purse in doing so.

The 19th century was an age in which such eccentrics thrived. Ludwig has been compared with the English eccentric, William Beckford, a millionaire also concerned with building and the arts—but whom nobody attempted to lock up. And there were others, no less eccentric than Ludwig. Perhaps it was because Ludwig was a king that people found his behaviour so unacceptable. Wagner was constantly imploring him to behave like a 'true king'. But he wanted to raise money to build castles and commission operas, not to make war. In common with many other sensitive, peace-loving people, Ludwig found politics boring, war horrifying. The pressures of kingship grew heavier, and Ludwig's unconventionalities were seen as signs of madness. Eventually, ministers hatched a scheme to certify him insane, driven out of all patience by his extravagant spending and his total indifference to matters of government, and his unpredictable behaviour.

The *Medical Report* on Ludwig sums up as follows:

1. His Majesty is in a very advanced stage of mental disturbance, suffering from that form of mental sickness known by the name of paranoia (insanity).

2. Suffering as he does from this form of disease, which has been gradually and continuously developing over a great number of years, His Majesty must be pronounced incurable and a further decay of his mental faculties is certain.

3. By reason of this disease, free volition on His Majesty's part is completely impossible. His Majesty must be considered as incapable of exercising government; and this incapacity will last, not merely for a full year, but for the whole of the rest of his life.'

It was an uncompromising report. Ludwig was made prisoner in the castle of Berg, near Lake Starnberg. Two days after his incarceration, the king's body and that of his manservant were found drowned in the waters of the lake. On hearing of his death, his cousin the Empress Elizabeth, was grief-stricken and appalled:

'The king was not mad; he was just an eccentric living in a world of dreams. They might have treated him more gently, and thus perhaps have spared him so terrible an end.'

Ludwig made a reality of fairy-tale castles.

WANTED!

FOR MURDER . . . FOR KIDNAPPING . . . FOR THEFT AND FOR ARSON

Can be recognised full face by habitual scowl. Rarely smiles. Talks rapidly, and when angered screams like a child.

ADOLF HITLER

ALIAS

Adolf Schicklegruber, Adolf Hittler or Hidler

Last heard of in Berlin, September 3, 1939. Aged fifty, height 5ft. 8½in., dark hair, frequently brushes one lock over left forehead. Blue eyes. Sallow complexion, stout build, weighs about 11st. 3lb. Suffering from acute monomania, with periodic fits of melancholia. Frequently bursts into tears when crossed. Harsh, guttural voice, and has a habit of raising right hand to shoulder level. DANGEROUS !

Profile from a recent photograph. Black moustache. inclines to fatness. Wide nostrils. Deep-set, menacing e

FOR MURDER Wanted for the murder of over a thousand of his fellow countrymen on the night of the Blood Bath, June 30, 1934. Wanted for the murder of countless political opponents in concentration camps.

He is indicted for the murder of Jews, Germans, Austrians, Czechs, Spaniards and Poles. He is now urgently wanted for homicide against citizens of the British Empire.

Hitler is a gunman who shoots to kill. He acts first and talks afterwards.

No appeals to sentiment can move him. This gangster, surrounded by armed hoodlums, is a natural killer. The reward for his apprehension, dead or alive, is the peace of mankind.

FOR KIDNAPPING Wanted for the kidnapping of Dr. Kurt

FOR THEFT Wanted for the larceny of eighty millions of Cze March, 1939. Wanted for the armed robbery resources of the Czech State. Wanted for Memelland. Wanted for robbing mankind of peace, of huma attempted assault on civilisation itself. This dangerous lun by spurious appeals to honour, to patriotism and to d when his protestations of peace and friendship are he is most likely to commit his smash and grab.

His tactics are known and easily recognised. wrecked and plundered by the depredations of without scruple.

Another Head of State, more dangerous than the artistic Ludwig.

FOR ARSON Wanted as the ince

Mental handicap - the confusion

The whole of this book is about mental *illness*. Hopefully, having got to this page, it will have become clearer what mental illness is. It is not a synonym for mental *handicap*. Illness and handicap are sometimes referred to together as mental *disorder* but the two are distinct. They need different treatment and different hospitals (psychiatric hospital for mental illness, subnormality hospital for mental handicap).

You *become* mentally ill. You start out by being normal, have a mental illness and, with few exceptions, become normal again.
You *are* mentally handicapped—once mentally handicapped, always mentally handicapped.

What is mental handicap if it's not the same as mental illness?

Put simply : brain damage or lack of brain development, which cannot be put right.

How does it happen?
Most people who are mentally handicapped are born that way. Sometimes there are genetical reasons for it, more often the reasons are not known.

Some people are left mentally handicapped by a severe physical illness, usually in infancy, which attacks the nervous system and so the brain. Some are left mentally handicapped after:
- accidental head injuries, increasingly often in road crashes.
- the heart stops pumping oxygen-rich blood to the brain, even for a few minutes, e.g. someone technically 'dies' and is revived after almost drowning, or having a heart-attack during which the heart actually stops. This is a rare cause of mental handicap, the crucial factor being for *how long* the brain is deprived of fresh blood.

Mental handicap has one thing in common with illness of any kind —there are degrees of seriousness. Just as all people who are ill are not equally ill, someone can be mildly mentally handicapped, or severely mentally handicapped, or somewhere in between the two extremes. Someone who is mentally handicapped cannot be cured but he or she can be educated and trained for a job within the limits of the handicap, again this depends on how serious the handicap is.

Why the confusion?

Partly historical, it is only comparatively recently (about 1900) that the handicapped and the mentally ill have been separated. Partly it is the tendency to lump everyone who is 'mental' into the same group. The press are continually guilty of this and so perpetuate confusion by not making the difference clear. Also both official and colloquial terminology, tends to confuse. Even the word 'handicap' is not widely used yet; it has only been the official word since 1969. Before that, and still in use, it was 'mental subnormality' now rejected because no human being should be categorized as 'sub' anything.

The words

Mental handicap = mental subnormality
Mental handicap = mental deficiency
Mental handicap = mental retardation
Mental handicap = 'backward'—when used euphemistically
Mental handicap = simpleton (old fashioned word)
Mental handicap = idiot (now scarcely used at all except in ignorance or as a term of abuse)

It's all a matter of degree, the fashion of words (retardation, for example, is still current usage in the USA) and people's concern not to stigmatize by using a word with unfortunate connotations. But each word gradually absorbs unfortunate connotations, so someone finds a new one every now and then.

The traditional 'village idiot', a grown-up who acted like a young child, was mentally handicapped; the man who thinks he is the reincarnation of Napoleon is mentally ill.

The casualties

Who and how many?

Since most mental illness is an extension of normal emotions taken or driven to extremes, a great deal of it never comes to light. It is contained within the family and often disappears of its own accord, before becoming serious enough to make medical attention a necessity.

By the same token, since many forms of disturbances are extensions of normal social or anti-social behaviour, there are some groups within society who would not be immediately thought of as having problems of mental ill health, because these problems are complicated by other more obvious factors.

So addicts of drugs or alcohol are classified as 'addicts' although the causes of addiction probably lie within personality problems (mental ill health) of the individuals concerned. It has been estimated that one third of all the people who go to make up our vagrancy problem have had psychiatric treatment, and another third are in need of it. Yet the predominant problem is their 'homelessness' and that is how they are labelled.

Between one third and a half of our prison population is thought to be in need of some sort of psychiatric counselling at least, yet their label is 'offenders'. So it is virtually impossible to divorce mental ill health from a whole range of other interlocking social and medical problem groups. The trilogy of vagrants, prisoners and psychiatric patients is particularly closely interwoven; a mass of people move around between prison, sleeping rough and mental hospitals.

When it comes to counting heads the firmest figures to go on are hospital returns of people in, or passing through, mental hospitals. In 1970 there were just over 105 000 people in England and Wales who were mental hospital 'in-patients' (that is *living* in the hospitals). This means that about one third of *all* National Health Service beds are filled by people with mental illness. Mental illness is the greatest single medical problem facing our health services.

The number of people actually in hospital because of mental illness is bad enough but to this figure has to be added the number of new patients attending psychiatric day hospitals.

Over 20 000 people are living at home but going to hospital for the whole day, five days a week for treatment and support.

Plus the people who become new out-patients. Very nearly a quarter of a million are going to a general hospital psychiatric out-patient department every week or fortnight to see a psychiatrist, to talk about how their treatment is working, and whether to continue it or modify it.

Plus the people who have been able to leave psychiatric hospital but are only able to do so if transferred into the care of local authorities. There are over 90 000 people who still need support, and perhaps accommodation, from the local Social Services Department, if they are to cope with living outside hospital.

For these groups, which are clearly identified as needing psychiatric treatment for some form of mental illness, the total figure is 441 000. This begins to define the size of the problem of mental ill-health. But it is only a beginning, because the figure represents *identified* mental ill health, which is being treated or counteracted in some way. It does not take account of the shifting armies of homeless drifters, one third of whom are thought to be mentally ill. It does not take into account the prison population, many of whom would benefit from psychiatric treatment for some forms of mental illness.

Even more important in terms of estimating the mental health of the community at large, the figure for people receiving some kind of hospital or local authority treatment for mental illness does not take into account the hidden numbers whose mental illness has not been identified and treated and *may never be.*

Recognition of mental illness

The family doctor's surgery is the 'front line' of psychiatric treatment. What happens in that consulting room in the course of the three or so minutes which each interview takes, has a crucial bearing on the amount of mental ill health identified.

People going to the doctor because they are uneasy about their emotions or their state of mind, often approach the subject obliquely and complain of back-ache, stomach pains, listlessness or difficulty in sleeping. The doctor may take the complaint at its face value, give a prescription and show the person the door; or, the doctor may dig deeper and

---

Mental hospital in-patients – age and sex profile

Of all in-patients 44% are men, 56% women.

Age	Men %	Women %	NB
pre—15	1	1	45% of all in-patients are 65 and over
15—24	4	3	23% of all in-patients are 75 and over
25—34	8	4	Women only begin to outnumber men
35—44	12	7	beyond the age of 65 (statistically
45—54	20	11	women tend to live longer than men)
55—64	24	17	
65—74	19	25	
Over 75	12	32	
	100%	100%	

Legal status of in-patients

It is very important to appreciate that the vast majority of mental hospital patients are in hospital because they have agreed to be and recognize that they need treatment.

Informal patients   94%
i.e. voluntarily in hospital and free to leave when they wish
Legally detained patients   6%
i.e. compulsorily held in hospital under the terms of the Mental Health Act 1959

SOMETIMES I FEEL SMALL.

AND SOMETIMES I FEEL LARGER THAN LIFE...

SOMETIMES I FEEL CRUSHED.

AND SOMETIMES I FEEL LIKE A KING.

AND SOMETIMES I FEEL LIKE A WIT.

identify what is really worrying the patient. Then again, the patient may be sufficiently confident to say, 'It's my nerves, Doctor'. In that case it's up to the doctor, who may just prescribe a tonic, recommend that the person 'take it easy', or possibly dig deeper to identify what is really wrong.

Some family doctors, alive to the complexities of psychiatric trouble, have estimated that 30% of their patients come to them openly or obliquely complaining of emotional problems. Other family doctors, usually the older ones, with little interest in psychiatric trouble, and no eye for it, would say that none of their patients come to them complaining about emotional problems and that everything is explicable in physical terms and can be treated as such.

These is also a hidden category of people with a degree of mental ill health who are the ones who simply put up with it. Those who stoically or fearfully never complain, never seek help, and just carry their disturbances or emotional problem to the grave. Some would say these people are admirable, with a proper perspective on life and its difficulties, some would say they are sad and tragic, existing but not living.

Is mental illness on the increase?

Despite popular insistence that it is, the answer is 'probably not'. More people are coming forward for treatment, particularly of mild emotional problems, but this is not the same as an increase.

The number of people who are in-patients in hospital is steadily dropping, while the number of people entering hospital, *but usually for a very brief stay*, has been steadily rising, but now shows signs of levelling off. The people who were in-patients before the 1959 Mental Health Act, have been coming out into more suitable homes and hostels in the community, while others have been going into hospital more readily for short, intensive periods of treatment.

On the face of it, this steady annual increase in the number of *new* patients coming forward for out-patient treatment seems to indicate an increase in the amount of mental illness. But, a great deal of the apparent increase is due to more people being prepared to be identified as needing help *and* family doctors making far more frequent diagnoses of psychiatric trouble and referring patients to psychiatrists for treatment for mild forms of illness.

It is reasonable to think that problems of mental ill health always existed in large numbers, but the family doctor did not pick them up, and anyway there was no point in picking them up, because services to treat them did not exist. Also, many people simply did not complain, out of fear of consequences like the County Asylum. It is also true that people are gradually realizing that they need not put up with unpleasant symptoms of emotional trouble as their mothers and fathers may have done, that they have a right to feel better. People complain of quite mild symptoms earlier and more readily than previous generations, perhaps because medical care is freely available and there is a greater reliance on tranquillizing drugs, and perhaps because attitudes towards mental illness are changing.

BUT MOST OF THE TIME I FEEL JUST LIKE ME.

SO I DRINK.

Causes

It was all beautifully simple when everyone believed that the antics of 'lunatics' were dictated by phases of the moon. Now there are lots of theories and not many facts. There is no history of detailed research into causes of mental illness and even now, especially considering how large the problem is, little money is set aside for research. So we really don't know what causes mental illness; we can't say 'He is neurotic because X' or 'She is paranoid because Y'. There are lots of theories which can be followed up in more erudite books than this one, but here in summary form are some of the factors in the background of mental illness.

Stress

If mental illness is increasing rather than just coming to the surface more often, the most quoted reason is the stress placed on us by an urban, competitive society. It's a simple, persuasive reason and, obviously, it plays a part; it is something which increases vulnerability to mental illness. Stress is an integral part of our jobs, of growing up, of marriage, of being poor, of bereavement.

But stress has always been with us. Is it more stressful to flog down the M1 from Leeds to London, than it was to take four days over it by stagecoach along muddy, bone-shaking tracks with the risk of being robbed or shot by a highwayman?

We have created more stress by accelerating the pace of life, and by living in crowded cities. But business has always been cut-throat (literally so in the past!) and life has always been a struggle, and was even more of one before the Welfare State. We are very adaptable animals. The reason we became dominant on earth was that we were able to mould and adapt our environment. Is there really any reason to think that we have not adapted to the rush and impersonality of the acquisitive society?

The great difference between the second half of the

twentieth century and any earlier time is in communications: transport and mobility, telecommunications of all kinds and the media. These may have helped to break down the pattern of tight-knit, self-contained communities but this was a process made inevitable by the Industrial Revolution.

The media, seen as an arm of the acquisitive society, gets a lot of blame for creating dissatisfaction, urging us to keep up and keep in fashion. But is there anything wrong with having rising expectations of life? The farm labourer digging a ditch in 1905, unaware of the world beyond his village, was not necessarily happy because he didn't know what he was missing. Our picture of him is rosy across a stretch of time. He experienced stress in his life, and hardship and deprivation, just as we all do and just as we *need* to do as a form of natural safeguard, a spur —it is one of the checks and balances of normality.

Stress plays a part in the causes of mental illness, but it is only a part. It can't be the whole answer.

Environment

Again, a popular explanation for the 'increase' in mental illness is said to be the unnatural environment we have created for ourselves. We live crammed together yet in isolation from each other. We live alienated from our neighbours with no feeling of belonging to a community, and there is no doubt that this is an important factor. People need to feel they 'belong'.

But the environment as a *cause* of mental illness is a theory confused by many closely-linked issues: the breakdown of family life—the end of parents, children and grandchildren living together as one family—poverty, poor housing conditions, unemployment, crime, over-large families, the use of drink and drugs as a temporary oblivion to blot out intolerable social conditions, poor educational opportunities, poor leisure facilities.

Mental illness is thrown up from the morass of bad environmental conditions but so are a hundred and one other forms of social and emotional deprivation, particularly in the decaying centres of our cities. Isolating mental illness as a problem in such a setting is a fruitless exercise because it is linked in with so many other social problems and you cannot say which came first: the loneliness or the depression, the poverty or the anxiety, the bad housing and the drinking father or the aggressive child.

In this context our system of classifying people for convenience by their dominant 'social problem' breaks down and becomes irrelevant. This is the world of multi-factorial problems in which we can cater for one problem only to find four equally serious ones rushing in to take its place.

Stress brought on by poor housing conditions is a frequent backcloth to mental illness.

Fatal neighbours

Early in the morning of 19th June 1972, Victor Eeles woke up after a disturbed night. He then got out his rifle and going next door shot his neighbours, Mr and Mrs Prescott and their daughter Marjorie.

Ever since the Eeles family had moved into their house in Brookvale Road, Olton, Warwickshire, they had suffered from the extreme and disturbing behaviour of their neighbours. Almost every night Victor Eeles, his wife Sylvia who was pregnant, and their young daughter, had been kept awake by a record player playing a single song at high volume over and over again. There was spying, eavesdropping, shouted threats and insults and false accusations. This kind of behaviour had forced the previous neighbours to move out, and even driven the former owner to threaten the Prescotts with a carving knife.

The Prescotts were in fact, known to be mentally ill. Both Mr and Mrs Prescott had been in mental hospitals and their daughter was obviously far from well, but in an effort to rehabilitate them, they were living at home rather than in an institution. Complaints about them to the police were referred to the Welfare Department, but the supervisory system appears to have been sadly lacking. The Welfare Department did not intercede effectively to bring help and relief to either family and the provocation of the Eeles family continued.

Victor Eeles was described by the prosecution as 'tolerant and completely inoffensive'. He said in court 'I hate violence. I hate rows. I will walk away, do anything not to cause rows.' But he could not walk away from his own home and as the situation worsened, he bottled up his anger until his patience finally broke down altogether.

After he had committed his crime, he could hardly believe that he could have done such a thing, but when his memory cleared, he went to the police, gave up his rifle, and confessed. He came before the court in August and received a sympathetic hearing. The charge of murder was reduced to manslaughter on the grounds of diminished responsibility. Many people testified to his good character and the intolerable strain he had been living under.

Five psychiatrists gave evidence at the trial. Mr Eeles himself said 'I just shot and shot. I was like a madman.' But perhaps he was not so much a madman as an ordinary person, provoked beyond any reasonable extreme. He found himself trapped in a situation where he could find no 'normal' way out.

> 'I inherited a vile melancholy from my father, which
> has made me mad all my life, at least not sober.'
> Dr Samuel Johnson 1709—1794

Heredity

Dr. Johnson may have been right. There is pretty
strong evidence to suggest that people can inherit
some forms of mental illness or, at least, are more
susceptible if there is a family history of it. This is
probably a genetic process (we are all an amalgam of
the genes of our mothers and fathers) but it could be
a pattern learnt by exposure and experience; that is
if you grow up in a household with a mentally ill
parent some aspects of the experience may rub off.

But this process is *absolutely not* inevitable, nobody
is doomed to mental illness because one of their
parents suffered from some form of it. There are no
hard and fast rules.

If there is any genetic inheritance of disturbance it
often jumps a generation. Our thoughts about
inheritance as a cause of mental illness are coloured
by a memory of history and a time when it was
common for marriages to take place within the same
royal or aristocratic families. Persistent in-breeding
resulted in a pattern of genetic abnormalities amongst
which could be included the regular appearance of
mental illness within the families concerned.

Predisposition

Some people seem more vulnerable to mental illnesses
than others and the reasons are highly complex. When
a psychiatrist makes a diagnosis of mental illness he
or she may say, 'There was some predisposition to
this illness on the part of the patient', almost as if the
illness could have been anticipated and is no real
surprise.

The reasons for this are varied but often hark back to
the environmental 'cause' of mental ill health. A good
start in life is important for any child's future —not
a good start in financial terms but in emotional and
social terms: being wanted, feeling secure and being a
participating member in a warm, stable family unit.

Clearly many, many people don't get this sort of start
in life but grow up quite normal and make their own
way with no more than the usual difficulties. In many
cases there will have been compensating factors, such
as a good school, a cheerful nature, a good social life
outside the family, some skill (perhaps sporting), which
bestowed status and offered a circle of friends and
contacts.

But some people (and knowing which are which is one
of the great question-marks hanging over the debate
about causes of mental illness), are badly affected
by their physical and emotional environment in child-
hood, and their emotional and social development
is marred by the experience.

They find it difficult to make contact with other
people, friendship doesn't come easily to them; perhaps
their parents shunned contact with neighbours and
friends. They may be shy, and caught in a vicious
circle in which shyness prevents them from acquiring
the social skills which could overcome their shyness.
They may turn inwards and adopt very solitary activities as an alternative to contact with others. Loneliness
may make them more vulnerable to depression, a lack
of social graces may make them more vulnerable to
anxiety and self-reproach, boredom and the need to
fill time may lead them towards obsessiveness.

*Fear of being outside,
agoraphobia, is not an
uncommon condition,
but it's difficult for
sufferers to ask for
help when they are
afraid to go out.*

A young girl before and after treatment for anorexia nervosa, *a psychological inability to eat, resulting in a skeletal physique.*

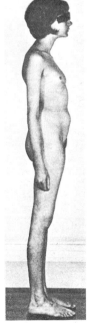

Tom Wright was always brim-full of confidence, often punished for 'being cheeky' when at school. He became a salesman, and a good one, and three years ago, when he was 38, was made Assistant Marketing Manager for his company. He was pleased, but, within a few months, it was becoming obvious that the job was too much for him, that he had been over-promoted.

Social drinking had always been a necessary and enjoyable part of his business life but his lunches began to become more liquid, and, after six months in the job, he had taken to keeping a bottle of Scotch in his bottom desk drawer. The work became heavier by natural increase, and by Tom's slowness in coping with the paperwork.

He had an affair with a sympathetic secretary and that, coupled with his mounting drink problem and the resulting shortage of money, made his wife leave him, taking their two children to live with her parents. Tom became very depressed, and stepped up his Scotch consumption.

His boss turned a blind eye to Tom's drinking but was quick to complain if his work was below par. His depression deepened to the point where Tom became almost completely inactive. After a half-hearted row with his boss about the standard of his work, Tom was fired. The sympathetic secretary urged Tom to see her family doctor who had him admitted to a psychiatric hospital with severe depression.

Tom was in hospital for six months being treated for depression and what had now turned into a serious drink problem. He is now back on the road for a new, understanding employer, is in contact with his wife and they hope to be able to re-establish their home and their life together in the next couple of months.

Tom in the case study above had some predisposition to illness because of the person he was and the situation he was in although the cause of illness included a high stress factor. For other people, predisposition to mental illness could exist because of their sensitivity or high degree of emotionality, which goes some of the way to account for the frequency with which mental illnesses affect writers, composers, and people in the creative arts.

Physical health

The mind and body are not separate entities. The mind does not just reside in the body, the two are inextricably linked together in function, control and performance. So it is not surprising that physical ill health can give rise to mental ill health, or that the workings of the mind can provoke symptoms of physical illness.

Apart from the psychosomatic disorders in the list of illnesses, it is understandable that someone could become depressed, for example, during the course of a long physical illness and need treatment for the depression as well as for the original illness.
An illness particularly prevalent among young women is *anorexia nervosa.* An ordinary diet to lose weight can turn into an obsessional revulsion towards food and a refusal to eat. People have starved themselves to death in this way. (Other complex factors may also contribute to this form of mental illness.)

Some people have phobias about the workings of their bodies, or the general condition of their bodies. Some

Sandra Wood's experience of mental illness was linked to her physical health but in a very special way—it was linked to the birth of her first baby. Sandra was 24 at the time and both she and her husband, Richard, very much wanted the baby. Sandra read all the books, did all the exercises, attended talks and practice bath-time sessions at the ante-natal clinic; she stopped smoking, ate all the right foods, watched her weight and generally looked forward to being a mother.

Her son Philip was born quite normally, at 8 o'clock on a Friday morning in March; he weighed 7lb 3oz. When Richard came to see her later in the day he found Sandra very weepy. He thought that was natural and didn't pay much attention when Sandra said she felt numb and uninterested in Philip.

Sandra had intended to breast feed but when the baby was brought to her she couldn't bear to touch him and the idea of feeding him made her burst into tears. The nurses had to give Philip artificial feeds and give Sandra tablets to suppress her production of milk. That was bad enough because she had so looked forward to feeding her baby, but each time the nurses brought him to her she refused to hold him.

With a terrible feeling of guilt it dawned on Sandra as she thought about it that she felt remote from her baby, he seemed almost alien, she had no feeling for him at all. Condemning herself as 'unnatural', Sandra spent the next day sobbing into her pillow, until her obstetrician came to see her. Between sobs, she blurted out to him how she felt and was amazed to find he was not shocked and didn't give her a lecture. In fact, he said her reaction was not unique and that depression after the birth of a baby took many forms, in her case it was a bit more extreme than most.

A few days later Sandra and Philip were transferred to a mother and baby unit within the hospital, a unit which also had psychiatric staff (all too rare, incidentally). Sandra spent a month in the unit having treatment for her post-puerperal (after child-birth) depression, and gradually coming to terms with Philip, and with being a mother. Feeling for him developed and she was able to go home with him. She returned to the unit once a week for the next two months and had a health visitor on call at home whenever she felt she needed her. Sandra's love for Philip now is probably all the greater because she had to learn to love him.

people have phobias about making love, for example, for reasons not associated with frigidity. And other anxieties, like the fear of impotence, which may have no foundation in fact, can become an obsession.

Hypochondriacs (people who are excessively pre-occupied with real or imagined ailments) can become utterly convinced that they are dying from a serious illness, most often cancer. Despite any number of assurances that they are wrong (and medical checks to prove it) they sometimes kill themselves rather than suffer the imagined illness. Hypochondria is a form of anxiety neurosis which focuses the nagging worry on to one specific thing, the person's own state of physical health.

PROOF!
YOU, TOO, CAN HAVE A BODY LIKE MINE!

ACCEPT FREE 7-DAY TRIAL OFFER

Muscles — with a full guarantee of quick RESULTS — are yours for the taking! You, too, can be a husky, healthy specimen of manhood that pretty girls can't ignore and that other fellows will envy.

PROVE IT! Find out FREE at no risk — post coupon below. In even the first 7 days you will see the amazing change in your body.

Gives you smashing stamina that can make you run miles without tiring, and handsome muscles perfectly distributed over your new body. The secret is 'DYNAMIC-TENSION.' It's the natural method of using the starved muscle-power asleep in undeveloped bodies.

Body obsessions can be turned to commercial advantage

'Look at Mr Blenkinsop! He's an assistant branch manager already.'

Poet Adrian Mitchell's breakdown was caused by extreme mental fatigue and lack of physical exercise. An early morning run was part of his cure. Now he has a dog and takes a regular daily breather.

Rhythm of life

A MAJOR American airline is keeping a daily check on the biorhythms of 28,000 employees in the hope of reducing accident rates. According to biorhythm theory, physical, emotional and intellectual ups and downs occur in fixed repetitive cycles that under-rate critical periods of stress. If these cycles can be predicted, one could guard against accidents as varied as cut fingers, dented bumpers, and major air disasters.

United Airlines takes the theory seriously. The rhythms of ground crews at National Airport, Washington, have been charted since November 1973. Accidents were cut by more than a half over a one-year period. Company supervisors warn employees to use extra caution on so-called critical days. Now flight crews are included in the check which is controlled from a computer centre in San Francisco.

'schizophrenias' group are biochemical in origin, and could eventually be treated biochemically when the mechanisms at fault are better understood and drugs can be developed.

The same is thought to be true of some of the severe forms of depression. But research in this area needs to be intensified before the jobs being done by chemicals in the brain can be understood, and a treatment regimen designed to counteract and correct the malfunctions.

Biochemistry

Chemical reactions are constantly taking place within the cells of the body and, particularly, within the brain. Contacts are being made and broken every second. Little pulses of electricity transfer messages from place to place, as we manipulate the complex computer of mind and body without even thinking about it.

This highly delicate and enormously complex machinery breaks down from time to time, and we become ill. If so many physical illnesses can be accounted for by chemical imbalances, the same must be true of mental illnesses. Or must it?

This is the greatest single argument going on within psychiatry today. Again, research is necessary for proof, and very little of it is taking place considering the size of the medical problem of mental illness.

Some research results are gradually emerging and there is evidence to suggest that some forms of illness in the

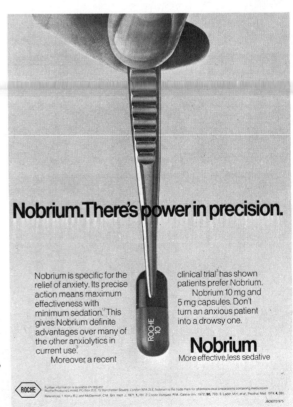

Every pill is a chemical treatment. Looking at adverts like this its easy to believe there is a pill for everything; a pill to make you happy, sleepy, confident—even a pill to get you through the day.

Escape from conflict

In another camp, across the river from the psychiatrists who think that biochemistry holds the key to unlock mental illnesses, sit those who maintain that mental illness is not *illness* at all, but simply the escape mechanism of the mind, when a person is faced with intolerable conflict within themselves or within their surroundings. This 'mental illness does not exist' theory says that what we call mental illness is a perfectly reasonable response to circumstances and events to which there appears to be no 'normal' solution.

It is impossible to show in a few words how such intolerable situations develop; you need to look very carefully at every aspect of all the relationships within the family. But look at the quotation below. It is from the mother of a girl diagnosed as schizophrenic. As a young child, everyone in the family agreed she had been a 'good' girl, no trouble in any way, but at about fifteen, she began to struggle against a family life which did not allow her any real independence. She began to criticize and say outrageous things. The family couldn't continue in its usual way, if the things this daughter was saying had any foundation of truth. Family life was threatened, and the response of its members was first to reject the formerly 'good' girl as 'bad'. It was still an uncomfortable situation though, until finally they began to call her not 'bad' but *mad*. A mad person can say painful things and nobody 'normal' has to take any notice whatsoever.

In this quotation the mother seems to be far happier with the idea that her daughter was mad, than that she could have meant some of the 'awful things she said'.

'I was beginning to hate the terrible things she said to me, but then I saw she couldn't help it . . . she was such a good girl. Then she started to say such awful things . . . if only we had known. Were we wrong to think she was responsible for what she said? I knew

she really could not have meant the awful things she said to me. In a way, I blame myself but, in a way, I'm glad that it was an illness after all, but if only I had not waited so long before I took her to a doctor.'

R D Laing *The Divided Self*

An understanding mother or one who is forcing her daughter into a 'mad' role?

This concept of mental illness is also sometimes called the 'scapegoat' theory. It suggests that one member of a family can be virtually 'singled out' for mental illness, or even subconsciously 'elect' to become ill, to avoid or perhaps resolve the family's conflicts.

'Is there anywhere such a thing as normal man? Modern society clamps a strait-jacket of conformity on every child that's born. In the process man's potentialities are devastated and the terms sanity and madness become ambiguous. The schizophrenic may simply be someone who has been unable to suppress his normal instincts and conform to an abnormal society'

R D Laing *The Politics of Experience*

Madness akin to genius

The artist Richard Dadd painted this picture in Bedlam in the 1850s. Having murdered his father, he spent forty years of his life in asylums. A sympathetic doctor encouraged his painting which became peculiarly obsessed with detail—some of which could only be detected with the aid of a magnifying glass.

Nijinsky

The tragic story of the collapse into madness of the Russian dancer Vaslav Nijinsky, is recorded in his personal diaries. Nijinsky's most creative period was during his twenties under the patronage of Diaghilev, the pioneer of modern dance. Diaghilev had a dominating effect on Nijinsky's professional and private life. After his marriage Nijinsky broke with Diaghilev. He made an abortive attempt to develop a new career for himself and finally settled in Switzerland with his wife and daughter. There he devoted his time to keeping his diaries and painting. Only a few years previously he had been fêted and courted by high society all over the world, but the world was changing; war was shaking Europe, and his native Russia was undergoing revolution. Nijinsky sought solace in religious mysticism, and grew increasingly withdrawn and eccentric. In less than a year, he was diagnosed 'schizophrenic', and with little help from anyone but his wife, he suffered the miseries of his illness, until he died in a clinic in London in 1950.

'I am God in man. I feel what Christ felt. I am like Buddha. I am the Buddhist God and every kind of God. I know each of them. I have met them all. I pretend to be mad on purpose, for my own aims. I know that if everyone thinks that I am a harmless madman they will not be afraid of me. I do not like people who think that I am a dangerous lunatic. I am a madman who loves mankind. *My madness is my love towards mankind.*

Vaslav Nijinsky, *The Diary of Vaslav Nijinsky*

Spike Milligan first caught the public ear with the oddball humour of the Goon Show, and has since written a number of books of quirky poems, stories and drawings. But while entertainment is his business, he has become more and more aware that there are two sides to his creativity. Bursts of imaginative energy alternate with periods of heavy depression. Was it that kind of a temperament that created the humour that made Spike Milligan famous? He is serious about that:

'It has been a cataclysmic disaster. I may have made other people laugh but I've destroyed myself.'

There was no peace for the old-style Hollywood star. Marilyn Monroe couldn't even have a cup of tea without photographers peering over her shoulder. There was mental illness in her family but whether it was that, the intense pressures of the film business or sheer accident that led to her death from an overdose in 1962 is open to question.

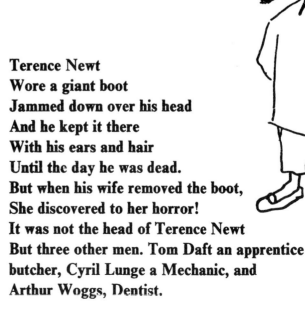

**Terence Newt
Wore a giant boot
Jammed down over his head
And he kept it there
With his ears and hair
Until the day he was dead.
But when his wife removed the boot,
She discovered to her horror!
It was not the head of Terence Newt
But three other men. Tom Daft an apprentice
butcher, Cyril Lunge a Mechanic, and
Arthur Woggs, Dentist.**

Treatment

> Macbeth
>> Canst thou not minister to a mind diseased
>> Pluck from the memory a rooted sorrow,
>> Raze out the written troubles of the brain
>> And, with some sweet oblivious antidote,
>> Cleanse the stuff'd bosom of that perilous
>>> stuff
>> Which weighs upon the heart?
>
> Doctor
>> Therein the patient
>> Must minister to himself.
>
> William Shakespeare *Macbeth*

Macbeth did not get much joy when he wanted treatment for his wife's madness; the Scottish Middle-Ages' version of 'pull yourself together' seems to have been the best advice available. Sadly it is still far from unknown even today for people to leave the family doctor's surgery wondering just how they should set about 'pulling themselves together' as the doctor suggested.

The family doctor is the first point of contact for anything you think is wrong with you—including your state of mind. He may treat you himself with prescriptions and counselling. He might ask a local authority social worker to get in touch with you, or arrange an appointment with a psychiatrist at an out-patient clinic at the general hospital. If you obviously need immediate hospital treatment, the family doctor will find you a hospital place in the usual way.

But, if you are convinced that you need help, or that some member of your family does, and the family doctor is unsympathetic and offers no treatment, you *can* go to see another general practitioner. (If you don't know one, the Citizens' Advice Bureau should have a list.) Alternatively, you can ask to see a social worker in the Social Services Department (the Town Hall will tell you who to ring to arrange this). This can be a daunting prospect since it is a formal and impersonal way of seeking help. However, it *should* be unnecessary as most family doctors are more receptive to psychological problems so you should not have to shop around.

Some views of treatment

'SOME YEARS AGO I took an overdose, found myself in a general hospital and eventually back home, face to face with my G.P.

"They pumped you out?"

"Yes."

"That will put you off doing that again."

I did not answer - what answer was there to such total lack of understanding. How could he understand that when one's *self* is dead within, a stomach pump is as nothing? Did he really believe that such treatment could prevent me from sinking into the abyss of despair again in the future?'

The GP is where the cycle begins. If he is helpful and understands that depression and anxiety, seemingly mild in his surgery, can lead to sheer desperation, he will take the matter seriously and refer the patient for help. If, as is the case with far too many, he is overworked and his time is pressured, he may well shrug off such symptoms and speculate vaguely that they will go away. The patient - or the relative - is left to sort himself out. If he knows enough about the ins and outs of the mental health services to wangle some attention without his GP's help, he may stand a chance. Conversely, he might find himself at the beginning of a syndrome, where he is sent from one brand of professional to another and ends up floundering in the middle.

I am a schizoid depressive and for the past twenty years I have been cared for by the National Health Service.

The NHS (which sounds a very impersonal title for the group of people who are my friends and there when I need them) has treated me with everything that's going: ECT, drugs, psychotherapy. For ten years I have paid regular but token visits to the clinic and I am technically still an out-patient. But in my twenties and thirties I spent months in the psychiatric wards.

Once, when I was having a particularly bad attack and had been given a massive injection, I had the idea that 'they' were trying to kill me. A small blond nurse passed the end of the bed and I moaned "Are they trying to kill me?" "No, luv," she replied, "We're not allowed to do that." And she smiled.

Everyone, from cleaners to receptionists to the nurses and doctors to the consultants has treated me with love, wisdom and understanding and I am more grateful than I can say.

Many readers of these articles will at some time themselves suffer from mental disorder: all will have close friends or relations who become mentally ill. It may, therefore, be of interest to summarise my conclusions.

1. Do not go for long term psychoanalysis: its efficacy is completely unproven and it is expensive and time consuming. It is just possible that it helps some people, but if it does not help you, give it up.

2. Try to find a psychiatrist though the NHS who is eclectic and not committed to one method of treatment. Different treatments suit different people and finding the right treatment is a matter of trial and error. Dogmatism in psychiatry in our present state of knowledge can only do harm.

3. If you feel you are seriously unwell mentally, do not simply accept drugs handed out by GPs—insist on seeing a psychiatrist.

4. New drugs can greatly alleviate suffering from mental illness, but it is dangerous to rely on drugs alone over long periods of time.

5. Remember that, for most neuroses, the spontaneous remission rate is quite high and the fact that you feel you will never come out of it is a symptom of the illness and not an objective truth.

6. It is not a disgrace to be mentally ill, nor need it incapacitate for life.

7. As a result of research both on drugs and psychotherapy new methods of treatment are constantly being evolved: there is therefore some hope even for chronic patients.

Dancing in the snow

Harry was a Fijian who had suffered from two brief attacks of manic behaviour. On each occasion he had been treated in a psychiatric hospital in the London area. As a result of these two attacks, he was aware of the symptoms which led up to them and, realising he was about to suffer a third attack, he visited the hospital where he had been a patient and asked to be admitted.

He was turned away, told to get a letter from his doctor. He had no doctor so he visited three other hospitals asking for treatment and each time he was rejected.

By now he was becoming manic and decided that the only thing he could do to get help was to behave in a mad manner. Taking off all his clothes, he danced naked in the High Street. A doctor and social worker quickly removed him to a psychiatric hospital under Section 29 of the Mental Health Act.

On admission to the hospital, Harry asked if he was any madder than the people who run the hospital service. He had been compulsorily admitted to hospital when this was what he had been asking for the past four days!

'WHY can't doctors treat patients as intelligent people who want to know what the diagnosis is, how the pills are to benefit, what their side effects are and what would happen if they don't take them - or take too many? Or have alcohol? A few words of advice is better than repeated prescriptions which affect some people very badly.' (Mrs. P. K.)

The people

Out-patient treatment (going to the general hospital clinic for regular appointments)
Patient may have contact with:
Family doctor
Consultant psychiatrist
Psychiatric registrar
Social worker
Family doctor (again)

Day-patient (going to a day hospital approx. 9am—4pm five days a week, or once or twice a week)
Patient may have contact with:
Nurses and an Occupational Therapist who will be on the staff of the day hospital. Otherwise the patient will see the same people as the out-patient

In-patient (actually having to go into hospital for a stay)
Patient may have contact with:
Family doctor
Consultant psychiatrist
Psychiatric registrar
Nurse (male or female)
Social worker
Psychotherapist (*possibly*, unlikely under National Health Service)
Psychologist (possibly)
Occupational therapist
Volunteer (possibly)
Social worker (again)
Family doctor (again)

Shortage of people to carry out treatment

Hospital for the mentally ill	Non-psychiatric hospitals
1 consultant per 154 patients	1 consultant per 31 patients
36 nurses per 100 patients	121 nurses per 100 patients

Key

Consultant psychiatrist—senior doctor: diagnoses, prescribes treatment programme, supervises treatment decides about discharge from hospital, etc.

Psychiatric registrar—also doctor but more junior: carries out treatment programme, takes part in group therapy (discussion)—the readily available medical member of the treatment team.

Nurse—usual training plus psychiatric training: makes relationship with patient, administers medicine, etc., takes part in group therapy—the main point of continuous contact.

Social worker—special qualification: helps sort out personal and social aspects of patient's problems e.g. family relationships, employment, housing, etc.; takes part in group therapy sometimes; again gives continuous point of contact and will help over the period when patient leaves hospital and continues support when patient is back in home setting.

Psychotherapist—usually a doctor with extra training: specialist in therapeutic technique i.e. group therapy, individual 'conversational' therapy, behaviour therapy etc. Very few working in the NHS.

Psychologist—not a doctor in the sense of a general practitioner, (a 'Dr' in front of the name usually means he/she has a Ph.D. in psychology): assessment of patient's personality, abilities; helps frame a recovery programme; takes part in group (and other) therapy; gauges aptitude for re-employment, etc.

Occupational therapist—special qualification: stimulate patient's interest in world about him/her as a rehabilitation exercise, brushes up rusty skills, teaches new ones especially those which will increase self-sufficienc

Volunteer—special ability rather than qualification: makes relationship with patient, provides a link with the real world and ordinary people, the person with most time just to listen and offer help and advice.

There is confusion in many people's minds about some members of the treatment team because of their similar titles—especially psychiatrists, psychotherapists and psychoanalysts.

Psychiatrists are not all Viennese with goatee beards, curious about your dreams, who ask you to lie on a couch and 'word associate' (sky—blue; blue—bottle; bottle—drink, etc.) for hours on end. They are doctors who have taken an extra qualification in psychological medicine and treat people who become mentally ill by whatever means are available (practical help, drugs, various therapeutic techniques) with the intention of making their patients well enough to return to every-day life as quickly as possible (hopefully, without the illness recurring although, of course, it may). The immediate concern of most psychiatrists is to control the *symptoms* of a mental illness so that the patient can function again in the community, although by no means all psychiatrists are happy that this has to be their priority.

Psychotherapists also are usually doctors with extra qualifications. But these are in 'talking treatment' and other techniques designed to uncover and then come to terms with the root cause of an illness rather than to control its symptoms, although psycho-therapy can be used in this way too. They do not use drugs for purposes of control but they may use them to make you relax and able to talk more easily. Psycho-therapy, with few exceptions, is available if you can afford it (and if you live in London: there are about five hundred registered psychotherapists in Britain, four hundred of them in Inner London). It is becoming gradually more available within the National Health Service but the development is *very* gradual.

Psychoanalysts may be doctors but they may not be medically qualified as such. They specialize in prolonged analysis (perhaps over a period of years) in weekly sessions —or as often as you can afford —of individual 'talking treatment'. It is the psychoanalysts who crop up so often in American novels and television, they are the therapists who seem to help half the population of Hollywood come to terms with their problems.

Unless you live in London, New York, or a similar metropolis, and have plenty of money, you are unlikely to be treated by either psychotherapists or psychoanalysts.

Most psychiatrists work within the National Health Service although some take private patients too (about £6.50 per hour). For someone who is very anxious about his or her state of mind, and finds waiting perhaps four weeks or more for an out patient appointment unbearable, one private consultation to put your mind at rest may be money well spent.

'Couch' cartoons have become part of the folk-lore about psychiatry (although cartoonists concentrate on psychotherapy and, especially, psychoanalysis for their material) and they often reinforce the unfair idea that psychiatry is something 'foreign', unreal and faintly ludicrous. Some cartoons use humorous licence in a damaging way to perpetuate the old suspicion that psychiatry is bogus, that it is a world of quacks and charlatans.

Sadly, for many of us, jokes and cartoons are all we know of psychiatry until we need help ourselves. What is *your* attitude towards psychiatry and psychiatrists? How have you arrived at these attitudes? If your family doctor suggested that you should see a psy-chiatrist,- would you go,-how would you feel about it,-what would you expect?

The places

The large Victorian mental hospitals arc a liability. They represent the attitudes and the fear of the past. They cannot overcome their external institutional appearance any more than the old general hospital can, but this need not mean that what goes on inside is at all old-fashioned. People should not be reluctant to seek treatment just because the local mental hospital was a place of dread in the 1930s. It is the same building but conditions and treatment methods have changed beyond recognition for the better.

Although the age and size of some hospitals for the mentally ill may seem daunting there are at least two levels of operation within each. A caring function has to be maintained for many patients admitted before the drug revolution of the 1950s. These are patients who have, or have developed over the years, a chronic or long term illness. These patients add up to 65% of the total population of hospitals for the mentally ill.

Each hospital also has special admission wards or units for *new* patients. These are characterized by fresh flowers, modern furniture, sleeping cubicles in small wards, pastel colours, pleasant fabrics, and a generally relaxed and friendly atmosphere. In these units, emphasis is on intensive treatment, so as to be able to return people to their families and jobs in the shortest time possible.

Psychiatric units are now being attached to the new District General Hospitals going up all over Britain. Out-patient psychiatric clinics are also held at the General Hospital rather than hospitals exclusively for the mentally ill.

Age of hospitals for the mentally ill
65% of British mental hospitals were built before 1891,
40% more than 100 years ago.

Size of hospitals for the mentally ill
Out of a total of 213 hospitals, only 48 still have over 1000 beds, only 4 still have over 2000 beds

Size of wards
Only 6% of hospitals for the mentally ill still have wards of 50 or more beds (the so-called 'back wards' for long-stay, chronic patients)

Length of stay in hospitals for the mentally ill
48% of patients—less than 1 month
81% of patients—less than 3 months
93% of patients—under 1 year

Don't forget the vast majority of people seeking treatment for emotional disorders are treated without ever being actually admitted to hospital.

The methods

Treatments for mental illnesses are essentially undramatic, if not downright dull. The exception is electroconvulsive therapy which is discussed later. Surgery is virtually unheard of now.

Chemotherapy—rather grand name for giving certain drugs and/or medicines by mouth or by injection.

Group therapy/discussion—talking; sharing problems and worries with fellow patients in admission ward and staff; 'getting it off your chest' as an aid to understanding origins of illness and avoiding circumstances leading up to illness in the future.

'Modified' psychotherapy talking; discussion sessions with specialist staff to try to uncover origins of illness and understand underlying reasons for it. 'Modified' because usually done in conjunction with chemotherapy and over a concentrated period of time rather than at length.

Behaviour therapy—talking; sometimes with simple 'rewards' (chocolates, magazines, or whatever the patient likes most) used to control and conquer unwanted patterns of behaviour such as phobias. A bird phobic would initially be talked to by therapist about phobia, then about birds, then (with a relaxing injection if necessary) pictures of birds would be introduced. Over a number of sessions, the phobic would be encouraged to hold and discuss photographs of birds, then feathers, then models, then stuffed birds, then caged birds and finally perhaps taken on a visit to the bird house at the zoo. It is a very gradual process by which the phobic is helped to overcome the object of irrational fear. Also very skilled business, DON'T try it for yourself or for a friend. Phobias may seem funny, but they are very real and very distressing for people who suffer from them.

Occupational therapy—practical activity to restore self-confidence; tailored to make a patient better able to cope with living independently in the community after hospital. Sometimes 'manual' skills especially domestic ones (cooking, dressmaking, woodwork), sometimes intellectual skills (current affairs, music appreciation, discussion groups about attitudes, etc.).

Art/Music/Drama therapy—encouraging self-expression through art/music/drama, providing an outlet for emotion and promoting better self-understanding. Not available in every hospital.

Electroconvulsive therapy—under anaesthetic, inducing a spasm by passing electric current through electrodes fitted over a patient's temples (like earphones). Apparently of value for psychotic depression and used in treating the schizophrenias. (See section on 'Controversy'.)

A doctor administering ECT (electroconvulsive therapy).

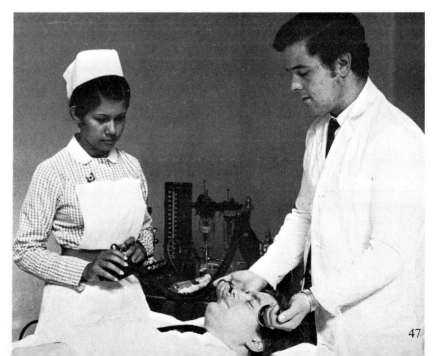

You begin by learning to trust. This exercise involves each person in the group leaning back in turn, simply depending on the hands on either side to hold them up.

One group forms a ring from which one member is excluded. This member then tries to rejoin the group.

Introductions—the group get to know each other's names and find out something about each other.

Drama therapy

These photographs show drama-therapy activities in an occupational therapy department at a hospital in East London. This kind of therapy is becoming increasingly recognized as a valuable form of rehabilitation. Patients of all ages and with a variety of problems participate in these activities.

This is a form of 'role-play'. The individual draws a face on the back of their hand and takes on the character of this face. It can be easier to speak freely using a 'role' of this kind.

Another form of role-play is where one person speaks through another, voicing unspoken thoughts and feelings. The girl places her hands on the man's shoulders and speaks for him.

Members of the group project their anxieties by acting them out with a cushion which can represent an object of hate, indifference, or love. You could for instance see it as a child and treat it gently. The woman above responds to it as an object of threat and beats it.

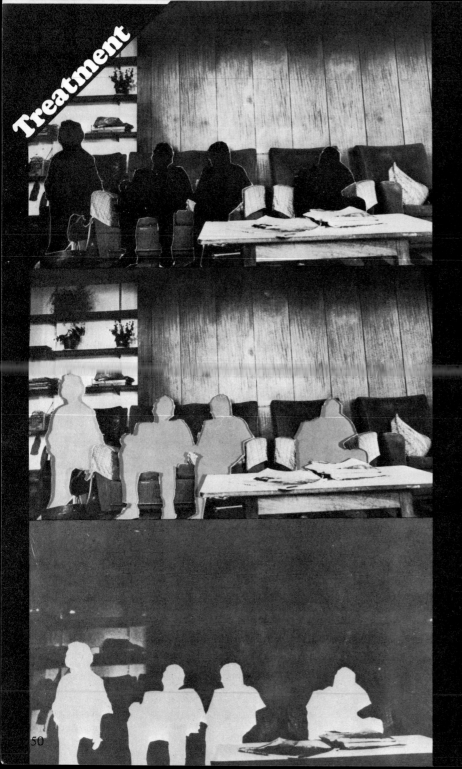

A day in the life of a patient in a first admission ward

7am Get up, wash, read newspaper, etc.
8am Breakfast
    followed by medication (pills, medicines)
    free time
9.30am Occupational therapy
    (or other therapies e.g. group discussion)
    until noon
12.30pm Lunch
    followed by medication
    leisure time
2pm–4pm Occupational therapy
    (or other therapies) Tea trolley comes round about
    3pm
4pm Visiting time/leisure
    until 7.30pm
7.30 pm Supper
    followed by night medication
    leisure
9pm Visiting/leisure
10 pm Bedtime
    Bedtime midnight on Saturdays
    Saturday and Sunday: no occupational therapy,
    more visiting, going home with relatives and social
    activities.

At any time during the course of the week a patient
can ask to see a registrar or a social worker, or both,
about anything worrying them about treatment, how
they feel, the situation at home, etc. There may be a
chance to talk to the consultant on weekly or twice
weekly ward round.

After hospital

As soon as treatment in hospital is no longer absolutely essential, the consultant psychiatrist will send a patient home or, if no home exists, find accommodation in the community with the help of a social worker.

The psychiatrist will continue to care for the patient at an out-patient clinic, at first weekly, then fortnightly, then monthly, over a period of a year or more. During this time the amount of drugs prescribed will be gradually reduced, and, in some cases, completely phased out,–some patients need to go on taking a controlling quantity of drugs for many years. The social worker will also continue to see the patient in his own home on the same kind of reducing time-scale, to help smooth out and solve problems of accommodation, employment, benefits, family relationships, and anything else which may come up.

The family doctor will resume normal responsibilities for the patient's health care when the psychiatric out-patient appointments cease, and it is to the family doctor or the social worker that a patient should turn for help if there are any signs of the illness recurring. The patient may well be put in touch with a variety of voluntary groups active in the locality, as an additional source of support during the early days after coming out of hospital.

The ability to cope for yourself in a home of your own and earn your own living is a very important part of getting back confidence after mental illness. Some concerned groups like MIND, local authorities and hospitals co-operate in the acquisition of houses where a group of patients on the way to recovery can live together with a minimum of supervision. After this some of the group will go on to live entirely independently.

There are also special workshops like this one where patients are making car-parts.

51

The controversy

Psychiatry is an inexact science, some would call it an art. It is barely fifty years old as a distinct medical speciality. It is difficult to tie down the causes of some mental illnesses. It is also difficult to be certain that psychiatry has yet discovered the best way to treat some illnesses, although there is broad agreement about how to handle the great mass of mild emotional disorders. The neuroses generally respond to treatment with drugs and a modified form of psychotherapy, with some on-going social and personal support of the person who becomes ill.

The controversy over treatment of mental illness really centres on the more serious, psychotic illness and the schizophrenias in particular. An increasing number of doctors and specialists, as well as members of the public, are questioning whether the schizophrenias are illnesses at all, in the accepted sense of the word.

The current argument in psychiatry is over the use of 'physical treatments', by which is meant electro-convulsive therapy in particular, and, to a lesser extent, the use of certain drugs as controlling agents. A minority of psychiatrists and other therapists maintain that physical treatments have no place in psychiatry, and a great many more psychiatrists have distinct reservations about the widespread use of electroconvulsive therapy (ECT).

Although ECT seems to be valuable for improving the condition of people suffering from severe, endogenous depression and sometimes for people diagnosed as 'schizophrenic', nobody knows for certain what happens when the electric current is passed through the front of the brain. It appears to help, therefore it is used. It is used in the absence of any more sophisticated and understood treatment being available.

It is sometimes referred to as a 'crude tool' of psychiatry, which needs greater refinement, and has to be used very selectively. It appears to speed up recovery, and, with so much treatment geared to achieving results and improvement in a patient's condition as quickly as possible, this is an advantage. But there can be side effects which, again, are not fully understood. Patients who have been given ECT are unsure of their surroundings for a time afterwards (not surprisingly perhaps), and suffer some temporary loss of memory. Some long-stay patients who may have had many 'doses' of ECT in the past are very docile, listless and apathetic. This could be in the nature of their illness. It could be the result of living in an institution for a long time. Or it could be because of the build-up effects of ECT itself.

The arguments within psychiatry about physical treatments have increased over the last 10 years or so. In particular the writing of Dr Ronald Laing has fuelled the controversy and made it public.

The controversy is as much about the objectives of psychiatry, that is whether the intention is to treat *symptoms* and get people 'back on their feet' as quickly as possible, or to discover and treat the *roots* of the illness, perhaps over a long period of time.

Of course, the patients themselves should have a voice in this argument but, because of the very nature of mental illnesses, they may be in no state to express a preference. (It seems fairly certain however, that patients could do with some more explanation of how ECT is administered. Many are frightened by the equipment and the procedure.) The whole issue is complex and ripe for discussion and is complicated by two factors:

When someone becomes mentally ill they and their families probably want a quick 'cure' if at all possible. In general, patients want to be returned home and to their jobs as fast as they can, rather than face spending what may be a long time discovering and dealing with the origins of their illness.

Secondly, it has been said that, to benefit from 'talking treatment' a patient has to be articulate and literate, that is good with words and good at talking about feelings and reactions to things. So what has tended to happen is that 'talking treatment' has become thought of as something for the intellectual middle-class whereas 'physical treatment' has become thought of as all that is relevant to the great majority of people. And debate continues about whether certain kinds of 'talking treatment' do good or harm.

The controversy within psychiatry is both encouraging and disturbing. Encouraging because there is always room for improvement. History has shown that there is no place for absolute certainty in medicine. Break-throughs are always being made, and there are many treatments we use which we do not fully comprehend. Disturbing because we traditionally expect doctors to know best and if they are seen to be arguing among themselves about treatment methods we have to wonder whether they really *do* know best.

If you became mentally ill, would your first consideration be to get 'back to normal' again, as fast as possible, or would you think it important to know *why* you became ill in the first place?

'What do you mean,
I should see a psychiatrist.
I am a psychiatrist.'

The way ECT (electro-convulsive therapy) is administered and explained to a patient can make the difference between a terrifying and a calming experience as these extracts from the novel *The Bell Jar* show.

'Doctor Gordon was unlocking the closet. He dragged out a table on wheels with a machine on it and rolled it behind the head of the bed. The nurse started swabbing my temples with a smelly grease.
" . . . Don't worry," the nurse grinned down at me. "Their first time everybody's scared to death."
I tried to smile, but my skin had gone still like parchment. Doctor Gordon was fitting two metal plates on either side of my head. He buckled them into place with a strap that dented my forehead, and gave me a wire to bite.
I shut my eyes.
There was a brief silence, like an indrawn breath. Then something bent down and took hold of me and shook me like the end of the world. Whee-ee-ee-ee-ee, it shrilled through an air crackling with blue light, and with each flash a great jolt drubbed me till I thought my bones would break and the sap fly out of me like a split plant. I wondered what terrible thing it was that I had done.

. . . I told Doctor Nolan about the machine, and the blue flashes, and the jolting and the noise. While I was telling her she went very still.
"That was a mistake," she said then. "It's not supposed to be like that."
"If it's done properly," Doctor Nolan said, "it's like going to sleep."

"Esther."
I woke out of a deep, drenched sleep, and the first thing I saw was Doctor Nolan's face swimming in front of me and saying "Esther, Esther."
I rubbed my eyes with an awkward hand.
. . . All the heat and fear had purged itself. I felt surprisingly at peace. The bell jar hung suspended, a few feet above my head. I was open to the circulating air.'

Sylvia Plath *The Bell Jar*

The special hospitals

When Ian Ball forced a car carrying Princess Anne and Captain Mark Phillips to stop in the Mall in London on the night of March 20th 1974, it was the culmination of two years of careful planning to kidnap the Princess. He intended to hold her to ransom for three million pounds. The money was to be given to the National Health Service, to be used to improve the care and treatment of psychiatric patients.

The kidnap attempt failed and Mr Ball was captured, but not before he had shot and wounded two policemen and two passers-by. On May 23rd, 1974, the Lord Chief Justice, Lord Widgery, made an order under the Mental Health Act sending Mr Ball to Rampton special hospital for an unlimited length of time.

The special hospitals are 'special' because they cater predominantly for mentally abnormal offenders (they used to be called 'criminally insane') and because they are a cross between a prison and a hospital. There are four serving the whole of England and Wales: Broadmoor in Berkshire (920 patients), Rampton in Nottinghamshire (1180 patients), Moss Side near Liverpool (395 patients) and—a new one—Park Lane attached to Moss Side which takes the overspill of patients from Broadmoor.

Ian Ball had a history of psychiatric disturbance and had been seen by psychiatrists at a London hospital many times between 1967 and 1972. He was diagnosed as a schizophrenic, and had had drugs prescribed for him. It had been suggested that he should become an in-patient but he had rejected the suggestion. At that time there were no grounds either because of his condition, or his behaviour, on which he could have been compulsorily admitted to a psychiatric hospital.

His action on the night of March 20th, 1974, was a criminal action. He faced charges at the Old Bailey of attempted murder, wounding with intent to cause grievous bodily harm, and attempted kidnapping. But in the opinion of the Home Office psychiatrist he was 'mad' at the time of the incident, and he went to a special hospital rather than prison, because the treatment he needed would have been difficult, if not impossible, to provide in prison.

People are sent to special hospitals (or transferred from ordinary psychiatric hospital) for many much less bizarre reasons. Mainly, they need psychiatric treatment but pose a security problem too. They do *not* necessarily have to be offenders, in fact, many people are in special hospitals for different reasons, mostly to do with the absence of alternative special facilities within the mental health service.

A thorough exploration of the issues involved in the treatment and care of the mentally abnormal offender and the workings of the special hospitals really needs a whole book to itself, but what is important here is to get the numbers involved into perspective when talking about the special hospitals. In fact, special hospitals hold a total of only two and a half thousand patients. Although court cases after which people are sent to a special hospital often hit the headlines because of their criminal content, and because they are frequently dramatic and extraordinary, such people represent only a very small part of the whole picture of mental ill health.

The patients in the special hospitals need special treatment in secure conditions at the time they are admitted. They may spend a long time in the special hospital, but —as with any other hospital —the treatment is geared to discovering what is wrong, putting it right and eventually returning the patients to the community and their everyday lives. Allowing people who were originally sent to special hospital for committing a criminal act to leave is a joint psychiatric and Home Office decision.

Attitudes

The madman with a stick in his hand was expected to be violent, and probably would have been, so Dr Johnson's reaction of self-preservation is understandable. But he is also saying things about assumptions and attitudes.

The assumption we would make about a madman with a stick is that he is going to bash us with it, not that he has been cutting firewood, or is going to unblock a drain with his stick, or prop a door open with it. The man's actions are going to be unpredictable because he is 'mad' so let's not take any chances, let's get in first, we can always be sympathetic afterwards. It is a classic 'shoot first, ask questions afterwards' situation.

Despite modern man's veneer of sophistication and tolerance, old-fashioned prejudice, and fear of the extraordinary and the unpredictable, is not very far beneath the surface. Mental illness is still widely regarded as extraordinary and unpredictable. We still retain the lurking suspicion that people never *really* recover from a *mental* illness, that somehow they are 'never quite right' again and the illness is liable to flare up at any time.

With this expectation of a sudden flare-up, we apply different standards to our assessment of the actions and behaviour of someone we know has been mentally ill. Anything unusual which that person says or does is weighed up and interpreted differently. Our attitude towards that person is coloured by our knowledge that mental disturbance is somewhere there in the background. If we did not know of the history of mental disturbance we would not give the same actions or behaviour a second thought.

It is no good saying that mental illness is *exactly* like a physical illness because, with a mental illness, there is always the unknown factor, always the tinge of mystery that surrounds the workings of the mind. If someone breaks a leg we know that it will be set, put in plaster, the leg will mend, the plaster will come off, the person will have to walk with a stick for a while before discarding the stick and being good as new. There has been a complex but understandable process of regeneration going on making the bone whole again. With a mental illness the mind has been affected and somehow the whole person has been influenced by the illness, or so we imagine. And who is to say that the mind has been 'made whole' again? Where's the proof? Show me the marks.

Our doubts about people ever making a true recovery from mental illness are supported and strengthened by the legacy of fear about mental illness. There is a stigma attached to a family with a member who has been mentally ill. There is an embarrassment about the out-of-the-ordinary; if the woman you are sitting next to on the bus suddenly starts talking to herself, how long is it before you move to another seat? or do you risk 'getting involved' by actually talking to her?

In a great many cases a person's complete recovery from a mental illness is very much dependent upon the attitudes of family, friends, people at work. A response from people, which makes allowances but doesn't labour them, is a vital link in the treatment chain. If the community is cold and suspicious, and rebuffs the ex-patient, the recovery of self-confidence and self-esteem is made immeasurably harder.

Gaddafi's sex smear

THE quixotic Colonel Gaddafi of Libya—can he be related to Idi Amin?—is now using **SEX** as a weapon against President Sadat of Egypt.

Quite remarkably, he has accused the **elegant** and civilised Mrs. Sadat of . . . wait for it . . . making a pass at him.

"Mrs. Sadat has tried to tempt me. But by the grace of God, I have resisted the temptation," he announced to his people.

He maintains that Mrs. Sadat showed great interest in him when he was President Sadat's guest in Cairo some months ago. She wore a tight blouse and skirt to show off her figure—and even sat in such a way that he could get a view of her legs.

She is a loose woman," he thundered pathetically away. "She is a disgrace to Arab womanhood. But this is not too surprising. Her mother is an Englishwoman and Englishwomen are loose." (Well, at least we got a mention.)

President Sadat is less than pleased. His reaction: "I could forgive this madman all his sins except his attack on my wife."

The final word came from Mrs. Sadat's mother—who is Scots (not English) and lives in Cairo: "The man is daft."

By and large, the community is not welcoming, which is why so many people try to hide any background of mental illness, just as they might try to hide a prison record —and the two things are not far apart in terms of acceptability in many people's minds.

There is prejudice from landlords or housing departments, from employers and fellow workers, from insurance companies and credit agencies. If ex-patients are open about their experience of mental illness, there is a none too subtle relegation into Division II of the Citizen's League. This is an erosion of civil rights which is absolutely unjustified, but at the same time, it is difficult to identify and take up with people or agencies involved.

Any suggestion of setting up a home or hostel for people from a psychiatric hospital who have no home, is greeted with public protest, neighbourhood petitions, public enquiries. Cries of 'We know they have to live somewhere but why here?' 'It won't be safe for our children to walk the streets', and 'It will put our property values down' are heard, as though people who have been mentally ill are a disreputable rabble, only fit for rehabilitation on some as yet uninhabited island. We have a long way to go before we can justifiably call ourselves civilized and tolerant.

We begin to learn our prejudice in the primary school playground when we learn to insult our friends with playful taunts of 'Screwy', 'Bonkers', 'Nutter' and, up until now, the prejudice has been reinforced at all stages of our social education. There are encouraging signs that the tide is turning a bit, as more and more young people reject implanted prejudices, and examine them in detail, before coming to any conclusions.

Why do we joke? Although there is a long tradition of humour at the expense of the 'madman', can we explain why we laugh? Is it uneasiness, relief that 'We're all right'? Is it nervous laughter, slightly shamefaced laughter? Or is laughter itself the safety mechanism we use to keep the unacceptable at arm's length

NUTCASE IN VIEW! 2p

Community care

If the community is still not welcoming towards a person returning from hospital after a mental illness, what did the Mental Health Act have in mind when talking about 'community care'? If 'community care' isn't the same thing as a 'caring community', what is it?

The idea was that people who became ill would be treated not in large, remote mental hospitals but in a whole variety of 'caring' facilities (small units, day centres, hostels, sheltered workshops, and ordinary homes) actually in their home community. It is getting on for twenty years since the Act was passed and local authorities were given the job of setting up this community care network, yet few authorities have been able to meet their obligations —few have felt enthusiastic about doing so.

For every 200 000 of the population the recommended facilities are:
120 places in day centres
An adequate proportion of sheltered workshops
40 places in hostels, group homes and other forms of accommodation.

A bit of research at the Town Hall and you could quickly find out if these facilities exist in your area in enough numbers. If they don't, try asking your Social Services Department why not.

Although Whitehall (and the Welsh Office) provide money for local authorities and local authorities raise money of their own by rates, central government cannot *tell* local government how to spend money, it may only *recommend* how to spend it. How the money is spent locally depends on the councillors the community elects as representatives and the councillors' decisions in committee rooms and the council chamber. The needs of the mentally ill have always

had a low priority, largely because so few people at a local level are speaking up on their behalf and pressing for their needs to be met.

If you think more should be happening in your area, write to your District and County councillors, or to your local Community Health Council, and organize a 'lobby' group to press the Social Services Committee for action. The mentally ill need your voice.

ORDEAL OF SANE MAN IN HOSPITAL 'CELL'

BUS conductor Barry Stephenson spoke yesterday of his "living hell" in a mental hospital.

Barry, 31, was locked up for three days after being mistaken for another man with the same name.

"It was a terrifying ordeal," he said.

Work

"Every time I told the male nurses I shouldn't be there, they wouldn't believe me.

"As long as I live I'll never forget those three days. It's made me so ill I've been unable to go back to work and I have nightmares nearly every night." Barry, who lives with his wife Hazel in a council flat in Hayley Hill, Halifax, Yorkshire, suffers from epilepsy.

He was admitted to the Royal Halifax Infirmary at the end of February after collapsing at his home.

After a week, Barry was told he would be seen by a psychiatrist but the appointment was broken and he was transferred to Storthes Hall psychiatric hospital at Kirkburton, near Huddersfield.

There, said Barry, he was taken to a small room where three nurses fired questions at him.

He went on: "I couldn't answer the questions and the male nurses pinned my arms behind my back. Naturally, I struggled to get free and they gave me an injection which put me to sleep.

Torment

"When I came to next morning I was in a small filthy room which was like a cell."

Barry's torment ended when a psychiatrist questioned him and discovered he had been mistaken for a schizophrenic patient.

He was discharged—and now the health authorities have sent him letters of apology.

Barry said he is considering suing the authorities for damages and has also called for a top-level inquiry into the incident. "My main concern is to prevent anything like this happening again," said Barry.

Mr. R. W. Ransome, area administrator for Calderdale health authority, said: "We have tightened up procedures to make sure nothing like this happens again."

The media and mental illness

Newspapers and television are in the business of reporting news. They try to present a balanced view of stories they cover but, in the nature of reporting, 'bad news is good news and good news is no news at all'. So in newspapers and on television most stories with a mental illness content tend to be bad news as far as improving public attitudes towards the mentally ill is concerned.

For a mental illness story to be strong enough to be featured in the media, its 'strength' almost always equates to its degree of sensationalism, its drama, its unusual content—as with any other good story in fact. So, not surprisingly, the media gave wide and prolonged coverage to Ian Ball's attempt to kidnap Princess Anne, his trial, his history of mental disturbance and his being sent to Rampton special hospital. Obviously the story had great public interest and had to be reported. Unfortunately it helped confirm many people's fear and suspicion of mental illness and probably adversely affected public attitudes to *all kinds* of mental illness.

Inevitably, 'good' press stories centre on the extremes of mental illness, the dramatic, the colourful, the dangerous. Since they are the only kinds of stories given much space in newspapers and time on television, they serve to feed people's misconceptions about the nature of mental illness as something wild, extravagant and mysterious. The readers and viewers cannot be expected to make a mental note that these cases are the extremes of the whole spectrum of mental illness, and the sad result is that generalizations are made, and all mental illness gets a bad name.

The case which has received the greatest coverage in recent years is probably that of Graham Young. He was sent to Broadmoor special hospital in 1961 for

Poison unlimited

First his pets, then his family, then friends at work were victims

Notoriety such as this is the exception rather than the rule at Broadmoor and the other special hospitals. In fact, of the total figure for in-patients in mental hospitals, the special hospitals account for less than 2%. And of this small figure only a very tiny proportion are people with a criminal background or a danger to others.

IT ENDED in the ultimate horror ... human suffering and painful death. It began with a small boy's discovery that it was 'much more fun' poisoning neighbourhood pets than collecting stamps.

Graham Frederick Young started his macabre career at the age of 11. A quiet, rather reserved child, recalled relatives last night. Always collecting 'the oddest things'— like dead mice and caterpillars. Nobody realised then that Young was executing his pets in poison experiments.

'Look I know we used you in our programme on Loneliness three weeks ago, but don't you think you'd better go home to your bed-sit now?'

poisoning his family. He was conditionally released six years early, and killed two workmates with poison. Again the story had a criminal content *and* there was added controversy over why he was released from special hospital.

Again, the Graham Young case could scarcely not have been reported, but it contained all the bizarre and sinister elements of an extreme example of mental illness, and inevitably reinforced the public's fear of mental illness and the worries about the dangers of allowing the mentally ill to return to the community as quietly as possible.

Television discussion programmes about psychiatry too have done much to emphasize the split within psychiatry, stressing the division between psychiatrists who believe in 'physical treatment' and those who are committed to 'talking treatment' only. The technique of a television discussion is usually to invite to the studio, people with opposing views, so that conflict is created and 'good television' results. This is the business of television producers. The impression gained is that all of psychiatry is split into two camps, whereas in fact, the great majority of psychiatrists are in the centre, committed to neither camp.

The RIGHT to be mad

In any discussion about the rights of the individual, you are most unlikely to hear anyone talk about the individual's right to be mad. We take for granted the almost divine right of experts and specialists to rush to the aid of the 'madman' and treat his madness—even against his will in some cases. Is it not possible that a person is happier in a state of what we choose to call 'madness' than he would be in the state of our conformist idea of 'normality' or 'sanity'? Might that person have virtually elected to be 'mad'?

It is rarely questioned whether or not society (in this case, in the form of psychiatry) has the right to intervene and try to change things. But there is a case for suggesting that social control, far from being something by definition 'for the good of the individual', is an invasion of privacy and freedom. Once again, it all depends on what is deemed to be 'acceptable', what is seen to be abnormal, and who is doing the deeming and seeing.

KGB threat to wife

THE WIFE of the Soviet dissenter Leonid Plyushch has been told by the KGB that, if she continues to provide the world with information about the drugging of her husband in the Dnepropetrovsk prison mental hospital, the doses will be made even larger.

When she visited him three weeks ago, he was being 'treated' simultaneously with insulin and triftazin, a depressant, and could hardly speak. She then wrote an appeal to the three American astronauts as 'a last desperate hope' to stop the torturing of her husband.

In Russia psychiatry has become debased into a virtual arm of the KGB (secret police) as a convenient way of silencing political opposition. In the political context of Russia the thinking is simple; if you oppose the State you must be mad, if you are mad you should be in mental hospital. No doubt Russian psychiatrists are not very happy with this line of argument in medical terms, but they are in no position to object and so psychiatry has become a way of depriving people of their civil liberties.

One notable American professor of psychiatry maintains that psychiatry has been used in much the same way in the United States and that attaching a label saying 'mentally ill' to someone can be used as a technique for silencing them.

Labelling

For someone to be treated for a mental illness, doctors have first to diagnose the form of mental illness and give it a name. This categorization is necessary for the effective 'management' of any patient —if we know what is wrong we can give the treatment that is considered relevant.

The problem with this approach is that many mental illnesses carry with them an in-built stigma. To define a patient as 'schizophrenic', is to attach a label which has a number of connotations. The label is a value judgement and a handicap, because people have preconceptions of what to expect of someone called 'schizophrenic'.

Is it fair to classify someone as 'schizophrenic' or 'manic-depressive' if that label is going to follow the person around for the rest of their life? Bearing such a label is often a short-cut to being relegated to Division II as a citizen, obliging the labelled person to labour under a handicap to achieve the same opportunities in life as the rest of us.

Anti-psychiatry and the quest for self-understanding

A lot of people today have become conscious of and interested in the workings of the mind, the process of making relationships, the significance of our feelings and the way we interact with people and the world about us. During the 1960s in America, and then in Britain, there has been a strong movement towards what is best described in shorthand as 'happiness through self-understanding'.

Within this broad movement, encounter groups, self-help groups and a whole variety of cults and sects have come into existence. Some are short-lived, some still gaining in strength but, partially, at least, they seem to fill the void left behind by the rejection of traditional psychiatry, a turning away from established religions and a general disenchantment with the existing social order.

Encounter groups are run by therapists of various kinds (outside the National Health Service) and are usually an intensive form of group therapy. They aim to promote self-awareness by trust, with people being absolutely open and honest within the group, so that each member can achieve new insight. It helps to be articulate but it is not essential.

Self-help groups are the most clearly 'anti-psychiatry' in outlook and are usually made up of groups of people who have tried traditional psychiatry as a source of help for their problem, and have found it unsatisfactory. They are often groups of people who bear the same psychiatric 'label', and who have set up their own self-support groups sometimes by living and working together in a communal setting.

So a substantial number of people today are seeking alternative styles of life and, in the process, working out new and personal definitions of mental health. It is too soon to know whether any of them has found

> However sympathetic you may feel towards those suffering from mental illness, it is always a shock to come face to face with it for yourself. Paradoxically, as the central character in the novel *The Four-Gated City* finds, it is sometimes the very labels that we use to try to understand it that keeps it at a distance from us.
>
> 'For years, all her life, the world of mental illness, and the doctors who dealt with it, had been alien. Not even frightening: it was too distant from her. Looking back, she was able to remember people: a friend, the husband of a friend, someone's mother, who had "a breakdown" of some kind. But she hadn't thought about it. Fear? She had been afraid? No. Because, from the moment it was said: so-and-so is mentally ill, so-and-so is having a breakdown, then it no longer concerned her: the words, the labels had removed them from her, whisked them out of her experience.
>
> . . . Yet, now, suddenly, because she was experiencing it, she felt as if she had been blind. For, suddenly, far from mental illness (as distinct from neurosis) being something that happened somewhere else, it was all around her; and, which was odder, had been all around her for a long time.'
>
> Doris Lessing *The Four-Gated City*

better alternatives since the movement is so young but, obviously, the people involved are convinced.

But a note of warning which has to be sounded is that sometimes very unhappy and vulnerable people are attracted to such groups, and it is debatable whether their unhappiness and vulnerability will be reduced or potentially increased by attachment to groups seeking alternatives.

The important contribution which society as a whole can make, is to be tolerant, to make room for alternatives and not to scoff at people who have genuine ideals which may be difficult for us to appreciate in the 'normal' run of things.

*Where will he go?
About 165 000
people leave mental
hospitals every year.*

National Association for Mental Health) is and so are other organizations and self-help groups, but still not enough people are doing so.

A far greater number of people have to take up the cause of mental ill health before there will be substantial political attention paid, funds released, and changes made.

The Government regularly issues guidelines and directives, laying down minimum standards for community care facilities, but local government can and does turn a blind eye to them. To be fair, the flow of money from central government is not steady; supplies of money to local authorities are frozen, and cut-backs demanded at times of economic difficulty for the country. All the same, unless pressure to meet the needs of the mentally ill is applied at local level, Count

---

Public and research spending on mental ill health

30% of all National Health Service beds are filled by people with mental illnesses, yet only

13% of the total resources of the Health and Personal Social Services are spent on mental health services

only 1·2% of the Department of Health and Social Security's research and development bill of more than £12 million is spent on research into mental illness.

Comparative weekly cost of hospital in-patients

Acute 'physical' hospitals £89 per patient per week

Hospitals for the mentally ill £30 per patient per week

It has to be said that hospitals for the physically ill are, by nature, more capital intensive (more electronics, more machines, etc) —even so the discrepancy is enormous.

The politics of mental illness

The history of mental illness in the 20th century is a history of neglect which persists into the 1970s. In political terms, those who shout loudest and who are best organized get the most attention for their cause and the resources and money with which to make things better. People who are—or have been—mentally ill, are not good at making their needs known. Many of them are not capable of doing so because of the nature of their illness, the majority of them are silent. So who *is* shouting for the mentally ill? MIND (The

and District Councils will be able to go on failing to honour their obligations to the mentally ill.

In political terms, everything boils down to priorities and how well a case for devoting money to one thing rather than another is made. Do we want a network of motorways, or enough social workers to meet the community's needs? Do we want another international airport, or a unit for disturbed adolescents in each region of Britain?

There is a strong motorway lobby, a strong airport lobby and a not yet strong enough mental health lobby. The way public money is used all depends on what you and everyone else thinks is important for the quality of life.

What, then, is mental *health*?

The pat answer to the question 'What is mental health?' is 'The absence of mental illness'—but that doesn't get us very far. Mental health, like mental illness, is a matter of degree. It is something for us each to define in our own way. Try making a list of situations involving your best friend and then try to decide what would be the 'mentally healthy' response to each situation.

If being mentally healthy is being free from anxieties then none of us is mentally 100%. Why should we be, any more than we expect to be physically healthy all the time? It is not a reasonable expectation to be perfectly mentally healthy, we all have ups and downs day by day.

Anyway, you have to keep in training to be physically fit so perhaps the same goes for being mentally fit. You can get to know yourself really thoroughly, question your reactions to situations in which you find yourself, question your attitudes and your preconceptions, admit your failings to yourself, be totally honest with yourself, keep fact and fantasy in your life firmly apart. It is not easy but it is a start.

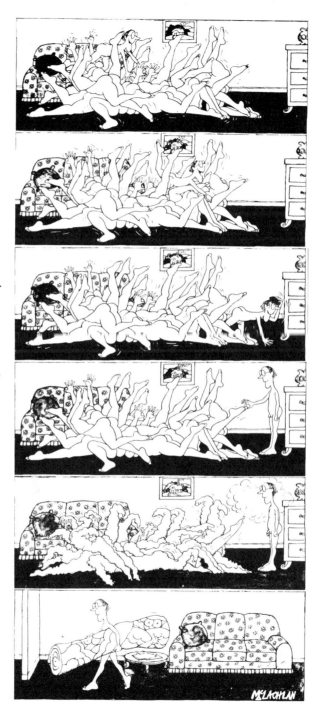

of ordinary people; people to give practical help, people to speak for them, people to help them fight their battles against authorities which may have to be made to demonstrate their care a bit more. Get involved in voluntary work on behalf of the mentally ill—they need you now.

What of your own future? We all have to learn and appreciate the value of making lasting relationships and understanding the forces at work within those relationships —at home, at school, at work, in every facet of our lives. Many of us are faced or will be, with the task of being good parents, an enormous responsibility and a long-term commitment. Do we think hard enough about the responsibility and commitment of becoming parents?

How can we avoid handing on our attitudes and prejudices to our children? We probably can't entirely avoid it but we can try to prevent our attitudes and prejudices becoming fixed. We have to stay flexible, and open to new ideas throughout our lives, and get our thoughts clear and based on facts—or the myths and folk-lore about mental illness will never die out.

'I have a problem . . . I'm always happy.'

However dull your life or your surroundings are you can always dream. One day perhaps an Elizabethan house in the country . . .

Getting involved

Promoting mental health means changing attitudes, changing priorities. It means broad education, and it means political action. These are long-term aims but they need to be worked for now.

For the short-term, for here and now, people who have been mentally ill often need the help and understanding